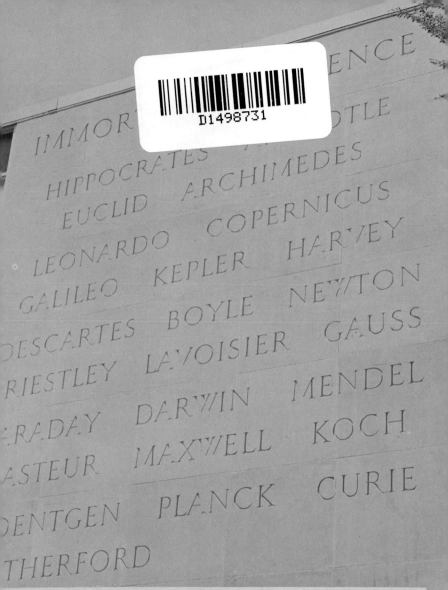

IMMORT... ...ENCE

ARISTOTLE

HIPPOCRATES

EUCLID ARCHIMEDES

LEONARDO COPERNICUS

GALILEO KEPLER HARVEY

DESCARTES BOYLE NEWTON

RIESTLEY LAVOISIER GAUSS

ERADAY DARWIN MENDEL

ASTEUR MAXWELL KOCH

OENTGEN PLANCK CURIE

THERFORD

he Science Wall of Honor on the Charles A. Dana Hall of Science at
e University of Bridgeport, Connecticut. This memorial was created
 commemorate and perpetuate the names of the world's Immortals of
ience whose fundamental discoveries in the field of natural science
ve yielded the greatest benefits to mankind's fund of knowledge and
ntinue to improve its way of life. A world-wide poll was taken among
ading scientists, educators and editors to select the names of the first
venty-five Immortals whose names are inscribed on this handsome wall.

LEONARDO
DA VINCI

Pathfinder of Science

Portrait of Leonardo da Vinci, after a woodcut published in Lives of the Painters, by Vasari. The Latin inscription reads: Leonardo da Vinci, Painter & Sculptor of Florence.

Immortals of Science

LEONARDO DA VINCI

Pathfinder of Science

Henry S. Gillette

PICTURES BY THE AUTHOR

Franklin Watts, Inc., 575 Lexington Avenue
New York 22, New York

To my wife Trudy

FIRST PRINTING

Library of Congress Catalog Card Number: 62-8426
Copyright © 1962 by Franklin Watts, Inc.
Manufactured in the United States of America

DESIGNED BY BERNARD KLEIN

IT IS natural that, within the confines of these few pages, many facets of Leonardo's extraordinary personality will be missing. That he was an artist, a man of letters, a poet and a philosopher are well known. That he was also a man of humor, as well as a prophet whose vision extended far beyond his times, are facts that I have also tried to include in this biography. There are many gaps in our knowledge of his life, and these I have sometimes filled with my own imagination to give some continuity to his story. Little is known of his early days, his period of travels after leaving Milan and his years in Rome. There is, too, a certain mystery in his relations to those around him, since our descriptions of him derive mostly from his often cryptic, personal notes and from biographers who wrote of him many years after he had died.

This book is about Leonardo the scientist, and to fully write of his many accomplishments would require an encyclopedic mind. My intent has been to extract the essence of his story in the hopes that it would arouse the enthusiasm of a reader to further his interest in those other, more fully documented books—and, above all, in the notebooks that Leonardo himself wrote.

—H. S. G.

Rome, August 1961

Contents

1

The
Shield

Dusk was beginning to gather in the valley at the foot of Monte Albano as young Leonardo turned toward home. Stopping by a rushing stream to wash the dust of the day's explorations from his face, he laid aside his cap and his leather pouch and plunged his hands into the cold mountain water. He felt the force of the current and watched the whirl and flow of bubbles around his bare arms. There was the same feeling, he thought, to the flow of air he had experienced blowing around the rocky crags of the mountains.

This evening, however, there was no time to sit awhile and think. He was in a hurry to get home. Hastily scooping the water in his cupped palms, he splashed it over his head and face, then shaking the water from his hair he rose and picked up his cap. He took a satisfied look in his pouch, slung it over his shoulder and headed down the stony trail to the village of Vinci.

Vinci was a small hill town situated on a spur of Monte Albano. Its castle and the bell tower above the houses seemed like sentinels guarding the slopes of vineyards and olive groves spreading down into the valley.

Leonardo da Vinci, which means "Leonardo from the town of Vinci," thought about his home. He knew that he had been born in Anchiano, near Vinci, on April 15 of the year 1452, to a peasant girl named Caterina. At the age of five, he had been sent for by his natural father, Piero da Vinci, to come and live at his family's house in Vinci, a comfortable and roomy place with a spacious garden. Piero, five years before, had married Albiera di Giovanni Amadori, a girl of sixteen. They had had no children of their own, and Leonardo was welcomed into the home with affection by his young stepmother.

When Leonardo was about eleven, young Albicra died, leaving a darkened and saddened house. Two years later his father married another girl by the name of Francesca Lanfredini. Although laughter and song soon replaced the grief, Leonardo never forgot the love of his first stepmother.

Also in the house lived Antonio, his grandfather, who

was eighty-five, his grandmother, his uncle Allessandro Amadori and family, and, best of all, his uncle Francesco. The da Vincis, who could trace their beginnings in the town back to the thirteenth century, had always been respected lawyers and landowners. Because Uncle Francesco was neither a lawyer nor a great landowner, the people of the town said he did nothing; but he tended the family vineyards, and, to the delight of Leonardo, he raised his own silkworms.

As Leonardo entered the main gate, he noticed that the oil lamps were being lit above the stalls of the marketplace, and the lively confusion of the last hours of business was in full swing. People nodded and smiled to him, for as a boy of fifteen he was already a striking figure. He was tall with long, auburn hair falling to his shoulders and his face was so charming that it was frequently compared to those of the angels painted in the chapels of the church. The music of his lute, the sound of his voice, and the gentleness of his person were such that all hearts and doors were open to him.

Tonight, however, Leonardo avoided the usual invitations to stop and chat. His father would be back from Florence; he had been going there more and more frequently as his fame as a lawyer grew. Now Leonardo was thinking that he had almost finished the assignment his father, half jokingly, had given him many weeks ago—so many weeks ago that he was sure his father had forgotten about it. At that time a peasant, whose skill in providing fish and game for the table of Piero's big household was greatly appreciated, had asked a favor of him. This man had a round, wooden shield cut from a fig tree and he had asked Piero to have a design painted on it for him in Florence. Piero, who had noticed the sketches his son was making of plants, rock formations, and scenes in his wanderings about the countryside, decided to test his son's ability and gave the shield to the boy. In the secrecy of his room, into which no one was allowed, Leonardo had smoothed and prepared the wood, and on it he was painting a monster.

Scrambling over rocks, through streams, and into caves, Leonardo had been in the habit of gathering all manner of creeping and crawling life. Patiently he would bring these home in his leather pouch and carefully study and draw them. Maggots, bats, butterflies, locusts, and snakes added to the confusion of the boy's already cluttered room. Everywhere he went he collected the things that aroused his curiosity; and as a result, his room was always filled with rocks, dried plants, flowers, the skeletons of small animals—and his pages of notations and drawings. Now Leonardo had combined the features of these small forms of life to make a monster—emerging from a dark grotto and breathing fire and smoke—a thing more terrifying than if done from imagination, for each feature was a duplicate of a reality in nature.

Unobserved, Leonardo reached the privacy of his room and emptied this day's collection on a table beside the shield. He lit a candle and examined his catch—a lizard and a large grasshopper. These would complete his picture; and, the most extraordinary find of the day—a fossil seashell found high on the slopes of a mountain! How did it get there? Was it a result of the flood about which his religion had taught him? Had an immense wave deposited this ancient sea-life high on the Albano mountains? Looking more closely he saw that it was a type of sea-snail and in almost perfect preservation. This he would have to think about and examine later.

Now, however, the picture must be completed, for he hoped to surprise his father in the morning. But just then, Leonardo heard the family stirring below and his father calling him to dinner. Reluctantly he left his table, made himself presentable and went downstairs.

"Ah, Leonardo," his father said when he appeared in the family dining room. "I saw Benedetto dell'Abbaco on the way in town and he tells me you haven't been to school as often as you should—is that true?"

"Yes, Papa—but I'm not doing badly."

"Signor Benedetto might agree, at least in your mathematics. He tells me you ask him questions that often make him stop and think. But Leonardo, you have other subjects—Latin, reading, and writing—as well as arithmetic. You mustn't neglect the others, my boy. But come—let us eat."

Together they sat down with the rest of the family —a large, prosperous, and happy gathering. When dinner was over Leonardo made hurried excuses to all the family, protesting that he was too tired to sing, and escaped back into his room. For a long time he worked, unaware that the house was growing quieter. Finally he laid down his brushes and his maul stick, pushed his chair back and smiled a triumphant smile. The shield was finished. Tomorrow he would ask his father in to look at it.

Conscious now that everybody had gone to bed,

Leonardo blew out his candle and opened the shutters. The night sky was a panoply of stars and only here and there was the dark loneliness of the valley relieved by pinpoints of light. Leonardo leaned his head against the window frame and stared at the blue infinity above him. What exactly were the stars? Did all of them move around the earth? What was the haze that obscured the horizon ever so faintly? What was that sea-snail doing in the mountains? Why? How?

The next morning Leonardo found his father and Uncle Francesco in the garden deep in conversation about their vineyards and olive groves.

"Papa, I have a surprise for you up in my room—can you come now?"

"Yes, Leonardo. What is it you have found now—not a better way to raise my grapes, I'll wager!"

The elder da Vinci put his arm around the boy's shoulder and went with him up to the door of his room.

"Wait here, Papa, until I say to come in."

Leonardo unlocked his door, lifted the cloth from the shield standing on the easel and opened the shutter just a trifle so that a soft light filled the room.

"Papa—you can come in now."

Piero entered—he had long forgotten the round piece of wood—and suddenly he froze in the middle of the room.

"Have mercy on me!" he said when he saw the horrible fire-breathing creature. In the dimness of the room, the monster and the murky cave from which it was emerging were terribly real. Piero actually started to back out of the room in fright, when Leonardo laid a hand on his shoulder.

"Papa, this work has served its purpose; take it away, then, for it has produced the intended effect."

The shield was the talk of the house; it was set up and marveled at. As for Piero, he resolved to take it with him to Florence secretly and sell it, giving his peasant friend some cheap substitute that he would buy in the marketplace.

So, a few days later, Leonardo's father saddled his horse and had the shield wrapped and packed in his saddlebag. Also, unknown to his son, he took some of the boy's drawings. Piero had now realized that Leonardo might have a rare talent. Moreover, he was planning to move to Florence with his family so that he could be nearer to the Badia, or the law offices of the city, for whom he had been frequently employed. There, thought Piero, Leonardo's talent could be developed under the best of teachers.

It was many days before Leonardo's father returned; when he did, he gathered his family together and it was obvious to all that he had exciting news. First, Piero announced that he and Francesca would move to Florence since he and a law partner were now engaged in securing office space from the Badia. It was a handsome office centrally located opposite the palace of the *Podestà*, or chief magistrate.

Then, turning to Leonardo, he said: "I have shown some of your drawings to Master Andrea del Verrocchio and his enthusiasm for your skill has decided me to place you in his studio as an apprentice. What do you think of that?"

Leonardo was stunned. Verrochio, the great artist and sculptor! Florence! The city-state whose power and influence had spread far beyond her own walls. Now he would study in earnest; now he would find the answers to his never-ending questions. He embraced his father and could say nothing.

2

Florence

THE Italy of Medieval and Renaissance days was not a unified country as it is today. It was, of course, part of the Holy Roman Empire, but the main governing forces in the land were in the city-states, of which Florence was one of the most powerful. A city-state was much more than a city—it was almost a kingdom in itself. Each had its own army, and very often there were large-scale wars between such city-states as Milan, Naples, Rome, Venice—and of course Florence. The Italians of those days considered themselves citizens—not of Italy as a whole—but of their particular cities; people coming from other cities were looked upon as "foreigners,"

even though they looked the same, wore the same style of clothing, and spoke the same language!

All the power, influence, and ideas of this period in history were concentrated within the city-states. A man might be a very fine artist, engineer, or philosopher, but unless he managed to bring his work to the attention of the ruler of one of the cities, he was likely to remain in obscurity. Thus it was that Piero da Vinci, knowing that his son would have to have a powerful patron if he was to succeed at all, brought Leonardo to Florence.

In 1467, when the da Vinci family entered Florence, the city had been under the rule of the Medici family for some thirty-three years. As it was in most of these city-states, the head of the ruling family—at this time Piero de' Medici—was in charge of the government of Florence and the surrounding countryside. But Piero was fifty-one years old and ailing, and he had only two years of life left at the time of Leonardo's arrival.

None of this was in Leonardo's mind as he rode with his father through one of the great, guarded gates of the city. He was thinking, not of politics, but of the fabulous sights that awaited him in this rich center of commerce and activity.

The narrow streets of the city were so crowded that is was necessary for the da Vinci family, together with their servants and the donkeys laden with houshold effects, to go single file. Leonardo rode behind his father, shouting questions, and, at the same time, turning his head from side to side so as not to miss a thing. Brought up in the solitude of mountains and valleys, and accustomed to the quiet life of a village, the boy of fifteen

Leonardo rode behind his father, turning his head from side to side so as not to miss a thing.

was overwhelmed with the excitement of the city.

The party was now making its way past the booths of hundreds of shops, past magnificent palaces built by wealthy merchants, and across squares filled with the produce from hundreds of farms. Every now and then, Leonardo caught a glimpse of the cathedral dome, one of the architectural marvels of its day. He had seen the cathedral with its bell tower and also the towering spire of the Palazzo della Signoria—which means the Palace of the Lords—from a hill as they approached the city. This palace still stands and today it is called the Palazzo Vecchio or Old Palace. But now these sights were lost to view in the midst of the narrow streets, other churches, flags, and the lines of washing that seemed to hang everywhere. Frequently, Piero's party was pressed against a wall as a procession shoved its way through a street. Sometimes it was by armed horsemen escorting a rich banker to some appointment; other times it was a file of cowled monks observing some saint's day and carrying huge wax candles before them.

After they had crossed the magnificent square of the Signoria, in front of the Palace of the same name, Piero leaned down from his horse and asked a blacksmith where Verrochio's studio might be. The man shouted above the din of clanging hammers:

"Everybody knows that shop, Signor—it's down that street and to the right! You can't miss it—ask anybody!"

The man was right, for the workshop of Verrochio was not hard to find. Verrochio was considered one of Florence's finest artists and everybody knew of him. He was a short, broad-shouldered man of thirty-two with a round face, shrewd eyes, a thin mouth and dark curly hair that reached almost to his shoulders. In his workshop were two other apprentices—young Pietro Perugino, who was six years older than Leonardo, and Lorenzo di Credi, a boy of eight. They all lived in the house together and, after Leonardo was shown where he would sleep and had put away the few things he had brought with him from Vinci, he was taken to the place where he would work.

Verrochio, whose real name was Andrea di Michele di Francesco de' Cioni, had taken the name of his teacher, a renowned goldsmith, as was the custom in the shops at that time. Verrochio himself was a skilled goldsmith. But to be an artist and to have your own workshop in the year 1467 meant being a specialist in many things. Into Verrochio's place came a great variety of artistic work—painting pictures, sculpting and architecture, goldsmithing, designing and making armor, creating decorated furniture, designing mechanical toys, and even preparing stage scenery.

Verrochio, of course, would attend to the greater creative tasks, while his apprentices did the chores of grinding colors, preparing panels for painting, making armatures for his sculpture, hewing to size the marble for a statue, preparing molds for casting, building models for a new palace or church—in fact, all the countless number of preparations to the finished work. Sometimes, if an apprentice showed extraordinary talent, he would be allowed to work on the finished painting or assist with the final strokes of the chisel. Verrochio was a busy man and a successful artisan. To further his own ambitions, he was now absorbed in the perfecting of mathematical perspective and the study of geometry.

The curious Leonardo had come to the right man. In Verrochio's workshop, where so many crafts were learned at the same time, his powers of observation were able to develop; his hunger to know about mathematics was fed. In Verrochio, Leonardo found a teacher who would encourage these investigations and urge him to study a wide variety of subjects. Leonardo now felt his lack of a fuller education. He started to borrow mathematics textbooks and to seek out men who could teach him what he needed to know. After each day's work was over, Leonardo would continue on into the night, catching up on his neglected studies and discovering for himself new areas of thought such as anatomy, movement and weight, botany, and another subject which was to occupy much of his later years—*hydraulics,* or the useful application of water power.

In these early years, Leonardo commenced his famous *Notes.* He had developed his own "secret" writing in his childhood at Vinci. These notes—consisting of observations, proportions, and reminders to himself —were inscribed on his drawings. They were, however, unreadable to the eye—until held up to a mirror. Leonardo was lefthanded and could write fluently in this strange manner. It could have been for many reasons that he did so—perhaps from a natural desire for secrecy, perhaps for reasons of safety from possible enemies. In those days, plots and counterplots of all sorts were commonplace—a rumor or a whisper in the right ear could destroy a reputation or financially ruin a career.

Leonardo was popular in Florence. He traveled with the young men of the town, and his handsome appearance and enormous strength (he could bend a horseshoe in his hands) made him a welcome figure in many houses. He continued to play the lute and the lyre. He wrote poetry, composed his own music, and sang with a pleasing voice. His blue eyes were kind and his manner gentle. He always avoided arguments and competition when he could. When he walked through the marketplace and came upon the caged birds, he would buy them—just to set them free. Indeed, his love of animals had become so great that he no longer ate meat.

During these years in Verrochio's service, Leonardo grew in stature as an artist and rapidly developed into a scientist of promise. He amazed his master when he painted an angel in an altarpiece that had been assigned to Verrochio. He painted it in the new oil colors recently acquired from the Flemish painters. So astounded was Verrochio with its grace that the master vowed he would never lift a brush again if a "mere child" could so surpass him. In this picture there is a tuft of grass beside a kneeling figure, also painted by Leonardo, which indicates by its careful attention to detail the amount of research he did before committing it to canvas. In other paintings he made beautiful drawings of a lily and studies of animals and crabs, giving a hint of what was to come. For, in these preparatory works, Leonardo could not be satisfied until he had thoroughly studied the characteristics of plants and animals in general. Later in life, he was to become more and more absorbed in these researches until they occupied the greater part of his time.

In 1469, when Leonardo had been in Florence only two short years, Piero de' Medici died and was succeeded by his son, the mighty Lorenzo de' Medici—or Lorenzo the Magnificent, as he was often called. Now the city of Florence felt itself under the control of a man who really knew how to use power. Lorenzo *was* Florence; nothing happened without his making it happen, and he became one of the most prominent patrons of art and scholarship in all of Italy. If Leonardo was to make any headway in Florence, he would have to make himself noticed by this new Medici ruler.

But Leonardo was not yet worrying about how to make himself a success. A young man of seventeen and still an apprentice of Verrochio, Leonardo continued to meet new friends with new ideas. It was at about this time that he met Benedetto Aritmetico, a prominent scholar and mathematician. It is probable that this man drew Leonardo's attention to the practical needs of industry and commerce so that some of Leonardo's energy was directed toward the study and improvement of existing machinery and the invention of labor-saving devices. At any rate, during these months Leonardo was walking the streets of Florence, wandering into shops and mills, making careful observations of all the various methods of manufacturing. The more he saw, the more he thought to himself that one man could do the work of many—if only he had the proper machine. He even made drawings of laborers with picks and shovels to see if he could determine by mathematics better ways to swing and hold the tools.

In addition, the particular problems in the engagement of joints fascinated Leonardo, leading him on to the study of more general problems such as the transmission of power by gears and the strength of materials. He also spent long hours studying geometrical theories and reading Greek and Latin classical works. Laboriously, he translated these into his own formulas and made comments about them in his notebooks. He attended the lectures of John Argyropoulos, a Greek, who talked of the Aristotelian theories of natural history, and who had translated Aristotle's *Physics*.

The study of physics opened to Leonardo a whole new world of ideas. He experimented with cogwheels, and with the improvement of ways to lift weights. He became fascinated with the then-known laws of friction and built a bench upon which he tested various devices for the overcoming of frictional drag; he also tested the natural power of one body to set another in motion. This bench with its rollers and weights was similar in principle to the one used by the French physicist A. C. Coulomb almost three centuries later. Leonardo was indeed growing into a man of genius. Now everything from the stars to the flight of an insect occupied his thoughts.

At the same time, he continued his studies of drawing and painting. Frequently he was seen in Florence following someone whose face had interested him— sometimes for the better part of the day—and then at night he would fill a page with sketches of this same person from memory.

By developing his powers of observation in this way Leonardo came to rely more upon his own experiences and less upon what he was told or what he read. This brought him into frequent conflict with the astrologers, the alchemists and even the Church. The astrologers were men who told fortunes by the movements of the stars. The alchemists, with their knowledge of chemistry, pretended to be able to talk with ghosts and to tell the future. These men Leonardo held in contempt. Although he was a devoutly religious man, Leonardo objected to many attitudes of the Church which he considered outmoded and which stood in the way of scientific progress; because of these objections, he was frequently called a pagan.

In this same year of 1469, Leonardo met the aging Paolo del Pozzo Toscanelli. Toscanelli was a famous physician, philosopher and mathematician who, just the previous year, had marked off on the cathedral floor the famous meridian line for determining the dates of the various Church holidays. The old man and the boy became not only the famous teacher and ardent pupil, but close friends.

One evening at Toscanelli's house, the old man showed young Leonardo a globe of the world. Much of it was marked "unknown," but Toscanelli had filled in some areas from his own careful calculations and from the stories told him by sailors and travelers. Visions of distant lands, remote mountain ranges and vast oceans filled Leonardo's imagination as Toscanelli spoke. Then Toscanelli tapped the globe to the westward of Spain, saying:

"Here will be found a quicker route to India than the world has ever known before." Then, turning to Leonardo he murmured, "You will see it happen, my boy, in your lifetime."

One by one, Leonardo's childhood questions were

being answered. Toscanelli told him much about the stars, the fossils of creatures long disappeared from the world, and how he believed the earth's early formation took place. He also taught the boy the art of drawing a map. Not only did Toscanelli greatly influence Leonardo, but the course of history as well. Ten years after Toscanelli had died, Christopher Columbus, struggling westward over the Atlantic Ocean, was using a map that old Toscanelli had sent him, carefully notated with all his accumulated wisdom.

Leonardo, in keeping with his own philosophy, tested all this knowledge with experiments of his own. Because astronomical instruments were rare, crude, and costly, Leonardo borrowed them where he could and later set about making his own. He went on to experiment with time measurements, devising the first example of the application of a pendulum to regulate a clock; by means of two springs, it measured the minutes as well as the hours. So for the next three years Leonardo worked in Verrochio's studio and continued his studies and experiments.

In 1472 Leonardo's name was inscribed in the Red Book of the Painters of Florence, which was the official *guild*, or artists' union of that time. But he was so poor that he couldn't afford the dues and hardly had the money for the necessary candles to be burnt before St. Luke, the patron saint of all painters. Although his father now had a spacious apartment in a house on one of the main squares of Florence, Leonardo continued to live with Verrochio. In fact, he stayed on past his formal training period for about four more years, grateful to the kindly man for the food and bed he offered.

3

A Studio

of

His Own

ON SUNDAY, April 26, 1478, the bells of the cathedral were ringing loudly over Florence, almost drowning out the noise of the crowds in the street. Shutters were being thrown open and people were shouting excited questions at each other. Distantly at first, but growing in volume, was another sound—an ugly one—the sound of an approaching, angry mob. Leonardo, holding a roll of drawings closer under his arm, stopped and listened.

Suddenly the questioning voices stopped. The bells continued ringing and now the angry shouts of the mob could be heard.

"Lorenzo is dead! Giuliano is dead! Death to traitors! Pazzi! Pazzi!"

"On to the Palace of the Signoria! They've captured the Archbishop! He's a prisoner there!"

"Get a ram and we'll break the door down!"

The people in the street were caught up in the surging mass. Already soldiers of the Medici were spreading out through the city. Cobblestones were ripped from the street, and swords, knives, and clubs were being brandished in the air.

Leonardo, backed against a wall of a house, was soon left in an almost deserted street. Still holding the drawings, he made his way carefully back to his studio.

As it turned out, Lorenzo was not dead at all.

It was on this Sunday that the Pazzi conspiracy had broken out in Florence. In the cathedral, the ailing Giuliano de' Medici, brother of Lorenzo, was killed by assassins. Lorenzo himself escaped with only a scratched arm. The Pazzi family were rival bankers of the Medicis and had joined in this plot with Girolamo Riario, a relative of Pope Sixtus IV, and Francesco Salviati, a long-time enemy of Lorenzo. A hired professional thug completed the members of the conspiracy.

Girolamo Riario hated the Medicis because they refused him money for his own ambitions, and the Pope opposed Lorenzo because Lorenzo was supporting raids against papal territory. As for Archbishop Salviati, he had for years nursed a personal hatred for Lorenzo.

When the assassination attempt failed, the Arch-

Leonardo, backed against a wall, was soon left in an almost deserted street.

bishop and Francesco de' Pazzi fled to the Palace of the Signoria for protection. However, the members of the Council of Florence, who were meeting, then became suspicious and bolted the doors after them. Both men were later killed by the Medici followers and their bodies were hung from the barred windows of the Palace. In the terror of the days afterward, eighty victims lost their lives. The Pazzi conspiracy also had an effect on Leonardo's future, as we shall see later on.

Leonardo had been on his way to the Palace that morning. He had been given his first painting assignment, or commission, the previous January. This was to paint an altarpiece for the chapel of San Bernardo in the Palace, and just the month before he had received the sum of twenty-five florins as a partial payment.

Some time before January of 1478, Leonardo had left Verrochio and had found a place of his own. The commission had come to Leonardo through the influence of his father, who was now one of the leading notaries, or lawyers, of the city. Though still poor, Leonardo could now devote this new independence to his widening fields of study.

Leonardo's studio was like his childhood room in one respect—it was still filled with all the different things that had aroused his curiosity. Books were everywhere —on his tables and shelves and piled on the floor— books by Ptolemy, Pliny, and Strabo on geography and natural history, by Aristotle on physics, even one by Guido, a tenth-century monk, who has been called the father of modern music. In addition, there were books on arithmetic, agriculture, geometry, grammar, philosophy, fables, poetry and even one containing jokes. A map of the world hung on the wall, together with his drawings; and, scattered throughout the whole studio were the plants, fossils, rocks and animal skeletons he was still collecting from his trips into the country.

There was also a huge table extending down the middle of Leonardo's studio upon which were many drawings and instruments for working geometrical problems. His easel near the window supported a painting—a study for his commission in the Palazzo. And on his desk was a confusion of papers containing notes all written in his "secret" writing.

At twenty-six Leonardo was deep in the study of mechanical law, geometry, and botany. For example, he had observed the rings in trees and their relationship to the age of the trees. In mechanics, he was absorbed in drawing models of a "variable speed drive." By meshing three cogged wheels of different diameters to a common lantern wheel, Leonardo saw that different speeds of rotation could be obtained at the same time. This same principle is used in the gear shift of modern automobiles. About mechanics Leonardo wrote that it was "the paradise of the mathematical sciences because by means of it one comes to the fruit of mathematics."

Now, too, he was starting to write about his observations on the flight of birds, the formations of clouds and the behavior of smoke in the air. He compared the flying of birds to the swimming of fish in the sea, and the flow of air to the flow of water. Two hundred years before Newton, Leonardo would define the principles of aerodynamic reciprocity, as contained in Newton's Third Law of Motion.

At this time, Leonardo had an idea for making the

Arno river navigable all the way from Florence to Pisa by the addition of canals, thus giving Florence an outlet to the sea. He also had thoughts for the improvement of irrigation in order to make use of land that did not have enough water. Nothing that Leonardo saw in his day's activities was too small to pass unnoticed and unquestioned. The flight of a butterfly, the stratification of rock in a cliffside, the shape of a mighty cumulus cloud, the turning of a carriage wheel on a bumpy road, the play of muscles in a farmer's back, the curling of water around a rock in a stream—all of these aroused Leonardo's curiosity. Continually, he studied these things and painstakingly drew them and wrote about them in his notebooks.

Unfortunately, Leonardo's painting commission for the Palace of the Signoria was never completed. By the end of the year 1478, the Pope, angered by the killing of the Archbishop during the Pazzi conspiracy, had declared war on the Republic of Florence. Ferdinand, the King of Naples, was persuaded to help in this war against Florence and the Medicis. As the papal forces were approaching the fortresses on the Florentine hills, the Council of Florence discontinued Leonardo's commission in order to conserve money for the defense of the city.

Disappointed though he was, Leonardo did not allow this setback to discourage him. From a page of drawings in the Uffizi Gallery of Florence on which are sketched various arms and war materials, we learn that he turned from his artistic to his mechanical skills and began designing engines of war. Besides being a Florentine con-

cerned with the defense of his city, Leonardo was eager
to gain an appointment with Lorenzo as military engineer to make up for the painting commission he had
just lost. Also, as the fifteenth century was a turning
point in the methods of waging war, Leonardo was
attracted to all the mechanical possibilities of the new
artillery. Before then soldiers had used spears, bows and
arrows, and stone-throwing catapults, among other primitive methods. One of Leonardo's designs included a
light cannon whose barrel could be raised or lowered to
proper elevation by means of a hand-cranked screw and
whose horizontal direction could be determined by a
maneuverable cradle.

The military appointment that Leonardo hoped for
didn't come. Unfortunately for the Medicis, the war
with the papal forces was being lost. One by one, the
fortresses under siege surrendered; more and more of
the Florentine troops were fleeing.

Leonardo continued the work on his military machines for, although he was having some success painting Madonnas for private homes and had even received
a commission from the King of Portugal for a tapestry
design, he still wanted official recognition for his inventions from Lorenzo de' Medici.

During these weeks late in the year of 1479, Leonardo conceived many ingenious devices to wage war.
Besides the small artillery piece, he designed a *bombard*,
or rock-throwing cannon, which did not recoil when
it was fired. This was followed by a light gun arranged
in three tiers of barrels, mounted so that while one tier
was fired, the second was being loaded and the third
was cooling (a forerunner of the modern machine

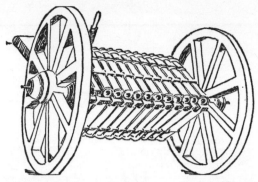

Leonardo's design for a machine gun. It had thirty-three barrels in three banks of eleven each. While one bank was fired, one cooled and the other was reloaded.

gun). Another was a device to repel enemy ladders. It consisted of a horizontal beam laid parallel to the top of a fortress wall; the beam could be pushed outward by one man or several men using a system of pulleys.

Unfortunately for Leonardo, just as he was ready to show these inventions to Lorenzo de' Medici, the last fortress outside Florence surrendered and a three-month truce followed. Lorenzo himself went to Naples and persuaded King Ferdinand to withdraw from the war. By 1480, peace returned once again to Florence.

As for the Medicis, military machines no longer interested them. Greatly disappointed at not having his inventions used—or even looked at—Leonardo began to search about for new fields of creative activity.

4

Years

of

Frustration

THE old monk spread the papers out before him on the table.

"Master Leonardo," he said, "these are the terms of the commission. We at the monastery wish to have an altarpiece painted for our chapel. Your father has recommended you, and, as you know, he is our lawyer. Of course your reputation has already reached our ears, and we are satisfied in our choice."

The year was 1480. The monk represented the monastery of San Donato a Scopeto near the Porta Romana, just outside Florence. Leonardo shook his head slowly at the terms of the commission. The painting had to be completed in thirty months at the most. Moreover, he must pay for his own colors and even—Leonardo looked up as if to protest but resumed reading—even pay for any gold or gold leaf he might use. Nevertheless, it was an opportunity, and Leonardo needed work. Since the papal war had ended, he had not received any commissions—and his skill at military engineering was still too unknown to have won him recognition.

Although Lorenzo de' Medici was a great supporter of the arts and sciences, he had not granted Leonardo any of his patronage. In Lorenzo's court were many men with much book-learning but little talent. They guarded their positions jealously and kept the way to Lorenzo barred to any applicant whom they did not like. Of them, Leonardo wrote in his notes: "They strut about puffed up and pompous, decked out and adorned, not with their own labors, but by those of others, and they will not even allow me my own. And if they despise me who am an inventor, how much more blame be given to themselves, who are not inventors but trumpeters and reciters of the work of others?"

In accepting the commission to paint the altarpiece, Leonardo hoped to attract attention to himself. Perhaps then Lorenzo might welcome him to his court and grant him patronage. So, with his usual thoroughness, Leonardo set about the task of preparing an Adoration of the Magi—a favorite subject of that time. This was to be a picture of the Holy Family surrounded by the three wise men from the East, shepherds and animals, old and young, rich and poor, paying their adoration to the Christ child.

Since he wanted his subjects perfect in every detail, Leonardo set about drawing countless youths, old men, sheep, oxen, horses, and donkeys. In a separate drawing for the background, he worked out with mathematical mastery the problems of perspective, that is, drawing objects to make them appear three dimensional and either close or far away in space. In addition, he made studies for the composition of the whole picture—studies in which his knowledge of geometry was used to heighten the excitement of this great religious subject.

Among these sketches that Leonardo made for his "Adoration of the Magi" is a page on which appears an inspiration for one of his greatest masterpieces—a drawing of the "Last Supper." And on this same page is another drawing—one of a hygrometer. A hygrometer is an instrument for measuring the amount of moisture

Leonardo's hygrometer.

in the air. Leonardo's design consists of a simple, graded disk with a balanced pointer, weighted at one end with sand and at the other with a sponge or some salt. As the sponge or salt absorbed the moisture in the air, the added weight was indicated on the graded disk, thus measuring the amount of humidity.

Leonardo's researches for the altar painting took him almost a year. Although the monks began to grumble at his slowness, Leonardo would not be hurried. He was determined to produce a painting that was perfect in all respects. To quiet their impatience Leonardo did odd jobs for them in the cloister. He repainted their old clock and for this extra work they advanced him some much-needed money. In March of 1481 Leonardo was ready to begin the actual drawing for the altarpiece. As he progressed with the composition, the monks crowded around with exclamations of delight. So different was it from all the other Adoration pictures they had ever seen, that the monks sent Leonardo some sacks of corn as a token of their appreciation.

One day, Leonardo was walking slowly toward the monastery over the Ponte Vecchio—the Old Bridge— across the Arno River. He made his way slowly up the hill past the construction for the new Pitti Palace. The morning was hot and the farmers moving into the city with their heavily laden carts were short-tempered. Leonardo stood to one side as he watched a pair of oxen straining to haul a wagon up a rise in the road. Their owner, his shirt unbuttoned to the waist, was shouting angrily, lashing the animals with his leather-thonged whip. It was a cruel sight and Leonardo turned away. From some experiments he had been making, Leonardo realized that the poor animals were struggling not only with the hill, but the drag of friction on the creaking axle. This drag could be eased, he thought to himself, by simply resting the axle in two sets of roller-bearings attached to the bottom of the cart near each wheel. In his mind he formed the plan for such a model as he made his way to the monastery.

The drawing of the altarpiece was nearing completion. The monks were fascinated by the spectacle of the Adoration appearing before their eyes. The soft, umber outlines deepened with gray, the ochre highlighting the central figures charmed them and they sent another gift to Leonardo's house—a cask of Tuscan red wine.

As it turned out, Leonardo never finished this altarpiece. It is not known why. But the drawing for it can be seen today in the Uffizi Gallery in Florence just as Leonardo left it.

It is certain, however, that Leonardo was far from idle during this time. He drew the design for eliminating the friction of a turning axle by mounting the axle in roller-bearings. He experimented with, and solved the problem of, transmitting motion to revolving machine parts by friction—the possible forerunner of our modern friction clutch. Another device, found in modern automobiles—the differential—was also drawn by Leonardo. This idea provided for the difference in speed between the two drive wheels when rounding a curve.

Leonardo also drew the first known plans for a self-propelled vehicle—an "automobile." It was designed to operate by a system of elastic springs wound by hand by the person on the vehicle; the "car" was then supposed to run the short distance allowed it by the unwinding of the springs.

In addition, Leonardo continued designing machines for both offensive and defensive military action. One of these was a breech-loading cannon, together with the first known projectiles that took into consideration better penetration through the air and greater stability in their trajectory. Indeed, these very much resembled present-day aerial bombs, with pointed noses and stabilizing fins.

As the months passed, however, Leonardo began to feel that his time and talents were being wasted in Florence. Although the monks and friends of the monastery were pleased with the work he was doing, other artists were being called to greater tasks in Rome. For example, Domenico di Tommaso del Ghirlandaio, Sandro Botticelli, and even Leonardo's fellow student, Pietro Perugino, had left Florence to work in the chapel of Pope Sixtus IV in Rome—known to us as the Sistine Chapel. Now, too, it was becoming clear that Lorenzo and his court had no time for this solitary genius whose ideas stretched beyond his age.

So Leonardo looked about him. He was thirty years old and the walls of Florence seemed to bind his spirit. To what city could he go where his talents would be put to fruitful use? Rome seemed to hold out no hope, for no one had offered him a position there.

But Leonardo remembered that there had been a visitor to the Medicis from another city in recent months. This man was Ludovico Sforza, the ruling prince of Milan, the great city-state of the north. Ludovico, who was also called "Il Moro" (the Moor) because of his dark complexion, was seeking the friendship and alliance of the Medicis. He was fascinated with the art and culture of Florence and sought to gather to his own court of Milan as many artists, scientists, philosophers, and musicians as he could.

Perhaps, thought Leonardo, his future lay in Milan. So he began collecting his countless drawings, diagrams of machines and instruments of war, his notes, his plans for canals and irrigation—even a drawing for a monument that he knew Ludovico wanted to erect to his father—and made a package of it to send to Ludovico. Then he sat down to write a letter to that nobleman. In it he set forth in ten numbered paragraphs his qualifications as military and naval engineer, architect, and hydraulics expert. Almost as an afterthought to the tenth item, he wrote: "I can carry out sculpture in marble, bronze, or clay, and also I can do in painting whatever may be done, as well as any other, be he who he may."

When he had finished the letter, Leonardo took out a strange instrument. It was a lyre of silver in the shape of a horse's head. He had designed it himself, and now with an air of peace, he commenced to play. Its rich tone was sweet to hear and the music was his own composition.

Leonardo had also designed other instruments—lyres, lutes, viols, and a kind of zither. He had perfected the single-stringed monochord of Pythagoras, replacing the tablet of wood with thin strips of drum that gave the instrument a low or high note according to the tightness of the string. In addition, he introduced stops or small pistons in the holes of wooden reed instruments; and, he had even invented a set of mechanical chords by using a wheel of reeds which plucked a set of strings as it was turned. His skill as a musician, composer, and singer was well known among his friends and his bass voice had retained the pureness of his boyhood.

As it happened, news of Leonardo's silver lyre had reached Lorenzo de' Medici. All Leonardo's paintings, all his designs for cannons and fortifications, all his inventions for commercial machinery had failed to interest Lorenzo—yet this single musical oddity excited the ruler's curiosity. Leonardo was summoned to the Medici palace.

Lorenzo was enchanted both by the instrument and Leonardo's musical talent. When Leonardo had finished playing, Lorenzo, surrounded by members of his court, applauded and said,

"It would please us if Master Leonardo da Vinci would present us with this beautiful instrument so that we, in turn, could make a gift of it to His Highness, Ludovico Sforza, of Milan."

Leonardo bowed and replied,

"Your Grace's request is my pleasure. Moreover, Sire, it would further that pleasure to bear the gift myself to His Excellency in Milan."

The idea delighted Lorenzo. He immediately directed that Leonardo be given a letter to Ludovico and that every protection be given Leonardo for his journey.

Leonardo, with the silver lyre and the letter of recommendation, hurried home to make his final preparations. He called on a friend and pupil, young Atalante Migliorotti, to accompany him.

Toward the end of 1482 or the beginning of 1483, with the letter to Ludovico folded in a leather pouch, Leonardo and Atalante mounted their horses and left Florence for the long journey to Milan.

5

Milan

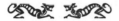

MILAN at this time was one of the greatest and wealthiest city-states in all Europe. Its battlements and the spires of its mighty cathedral rose impressively from the lush plain of Lombardy. Towering over the city in the distance were the snow-capped peaks of the Alps. Groves of mulberry trees for the production of its famous silk industry and vast stretches of rice paddies extended far into the surrounding countryside.

Leonardo and Atalante rode along the embankment of one of the many canals. The sight of the city hastened their pace although the journey had been a long one. Frequently on the trip Leonardo had stopped to make notes. Riding over the mountains and ravines surrounding Florence he had drawn some of the rushing streams and the stratifications of exposed cliffs. And when they had descended to the plains he observed the irrigation ditches and made notes on ways of improving the crude systems of dams and waterwheels.

Leonardo was excited by this new city and by his prospects at the court of Ludovico. On the way to his lodgings, he also noticed that Milan was a great center of arms manufacture. Shop after shop displayed its wares of swords, spears, shields, armor for man and horse, and signs advertising foundries for the making of cannon. Perhaps here he might find an outlet for his military inventions.

In the inn where he and Atalante stayed, Leonardo overheard the current political rumors. All around him was talk of the war. Girolamo Riario was again in the field, and Ludovico's ally, Alfonso of Calabria, had just been defeated by the Venetians in a bloody battle at Campo Morto.

Leonardo reread the letter he had written setting forth his own accomplishments and decided that now was the time to present himself as a military engineer. He would minimize the bronze monument, his music, and his painting, and instead, he would stress his skills in the inventions of war.

When Leonardo appeared before Ludovico, he was a handsome young man of thirty-one. Tall and strong, he was dressed not according to fashion, but simply—almost severely. His hair hung in curls on his shoulders and his auburn mustache and neatly trimmed beard accented his ruddy complexion and deep-set blue eyes.

Indeed, he presented a striking contrast to the noble-man seated before him. Il Moro, with his dark skin and straight black hair, his richly embroidered doublet with its broad sleeves and the heavy gold chains across his thick chest, was the exact opposite of Leonardo.

Ludovico set aside Leonardo's letter, rose from his chair, and walked to the heavy table on which Leonardo had spread out his drawings.

Plans for all manner of war machines were there—those that Leonardo had designed for Lorenzo de' Medici without success, together with many new additions. For example, there were plans for a self-propelled bomb with flames to be shot out in all directions—a bomb that was later to be called a "rotatory rocket" when it was actually invented in 1846. Leonardo also explained to Ludovico his idea for "poison gas" bombs containing sulfur: the fumes of these bombs would "produce stupor," and they could be used both on land and sea, together with masks to protect those who were using them. Shrapnel shells, hand grenades, and javelins that burst into flame when they struck their objectives—these and many more were among his ideas.

But perhaps the most unusual to Ludovico's eyes was the design for an armored vehicle. It was shaped like a giant turtle, with overlapping sheets of reinforced wood so that enemy shells would bounce off its surface. The armor was pierced by loopholes for the breech-loading cannon and there was an opening at the top for ventilation. Power for the vehicle was supplied by eight men inside turning cranks which in turn were cogged to other wheels, setting in motion the four drive wheels.

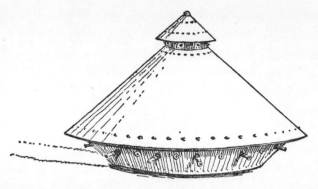

Forerunner of the tank or armored car, as conceived by Leonardo. Motion was supposed to be supplied by four cogged wheels turned by manpower. Sheets of reinforced wood were supposed to serve as "armor" against enemy projectiles.

This of course was the forerunner of the tank and the armored car used in modern warfare.

In addition, Leonardo laid before Ludovico all manner of cannons and designs for tunneling under the enemy's defenses. Actually, with respect to warfare itself, Leonardo called it a most brutal "madness"; however, he recognized the necessity of being prepared. In his notebook, he wrote, "When besieged by ambitious tyrants I find a means of offense and defense in order to preserve the chief gift of nature, which is liberty."

Ludovico was very much interested in the things Leonardo had showed him. Although he was a man of limited imagination and was not able to grasp the scope of Leonardo's proposals, he was nevertheless involved in a war. Since Ludovico's aging military engineer was to be replaced, Leonardo left the forbidding castle of the Sforzas with high hopes of getting the position.

In the meantime, he was commissioned to paint the portrait of a young girl from a noble family in Milan. At the same time, he began the bronze equestrian statue of Ludovico's father, Francesco Sforza. For this work, he began an intensive study of horses. Since hunting was the popular sport at the court of the Sforzas, Ludovico owned a stable of the finest Arabian horses, and here Leonardo commenced his drawings. Again, his research for a work of art led him beyond just making preparatory sketches. His studies developed into notes, and his notes into a planned book on the anatomy of the horse.

During these months of waiting for the appointment as military engineer, Leonardo furthered his experiments with cannon. In the course of these experiments, he came across a power that would later revolutionize all industry—steam. He devised—although he attributed the original idea to Archimedes—a water vessel connected to a copper tube which was heated by a fire. The water when flowing into the red-hot tube changed into steam and the pressure of the steam blew out a ball at the mouth of the tube with great force. Leonardo experimented with steam in other ways. He built an apparatus for measuring the transformation of water into vapor. It consisted of a metal box in which was a thin animal bladder partly filled with water. Resting on the top of the bladder was a flat lid attached by a cord hung from two pulleys to a counterweight on the outside. As the water was heated, the steam in the bladder pushed up the lid. As the lid rose both the volume and the pressure could be measured. There were distillation experiments with various condensers, one in particular that anticipated the modern condenser of Leibig, introducing double walls that formed a complete jacket for cooling with water in continual circulation.

Not content with having an idle moment, Leonardo again turned to searching out books that he had not read and trying to fill the gaps in his education. He became especially interested in the German philosopher, Cardinal Cusanus. Cusanus, like himself, had been influenced by Toscanelli and was a man devoted to the natural sciences. Leonardo also studied the philosophy of Aristotle and the writings of St. Augustine. Throughout his life Leonardo believed in an active mind for, as "iron rusts from disuse, stagnant water loses its purity and in cold weather becomes frozen, even so does inaction sap the vigor of the mind."

Unfortunately, the post of military engineer went to a man named Ambrogio Ferrari. The extent and variety of Leonardo's proposals were too great for Ludovico to trust. He did not believe that one man could possibly bring all those ideas into being. Ferrari, on the other hand, was a military engineer only, and a man who was content with the customary methods of warfare. Furthermore, Ludovico had at last decided that peaceful negotiations would gain him more than fighting. Thus Leonardo's chance of recognition was again postponed.

Meanwhile, the money that Leonardo had brought with him from Florence was almost gone. He had been forced to move from his apartment to a single room and now he was barely able to live from day to day. Although the court of Ludovico Sforza was one of the richest in the world, artists were frequently treated as servants; often they were the last to be paid for their services. Also, Leonardo was a foreigner in the city, which meant he was regarded with suspicion.

Because of these reasons, Leonardo finally decided to do what the Milanese artists did—they banded together in groups sharing work and costs. Leonardo had met a young artist of twenty-eight, Giovanni Ambrogio de Predis, at the court of Ludovico. Ambrogio was court painter to the Sforza family and had achieved some success. Ambrogio recognized in the handsome stranger from Florence, however, the touch of genius, and he realized that his own talents would be furthered by learning from Leonardo. The two young men decided to pool their abilities. Ambrogio offered both lodging and a studio; and, in association with his two half-brothers, one a woodcarver, another a miniaturist, and his elder brother, a minter of coins, they would not lack for commissions.

Commissions weren't long in coming. On April 25, 1483, a contract was signed between Bartolommeo degli Scarlione, a prior of the Fraternity of the Immaculate Conception, and Ambrogio and Leonardo for an altarpiece. The fee was two hundred ducats, with a promise of more if it were delivered on time and was satisfactory to the Fraternity. Delivery date was to be December 8, 1484. Ambrogio was to paint the altar wings and Leonardo the center piece—a picture of the Blessed Virgin and Child.

But when the painting was finished, it was not according to the instructions set forth in the contract. Leonardo had too independent a mind to be bound by conformity. Nor was it completed on time. Indeed, for twenty years the quarrel between the Fraternity and the painters went on. After ten years, Ludovico was asked to intervene for the money owed; after he failed, another ten years went by and the King of France himself was finally asked to settle the dispute. Leonardo wanted his one hundred ducats and the Fraternity offered twenty-five. Eventually, a secret agreement was arrived at and the painting was restored to Leonardo and Ambrogio. Leonardo's painting, the masterpiece entitled the "Virgin of the Rocks," now hangs in the museum of the Louvre in Paris.

The day this contract was signed, Leonardo walked back through the city to Ambrogio's studio near the Ticino gate. He was low in spirits from reading the petty instructions of the contract, and, in this mood, he became aware of the city streets and crowds about him. The noise, the confusion, the smells—yes, the smells were the worst. Garbage, filth, and dust were in heaps where the last rainwater had left them and they buzzed with flies.

Moreover the houses were jammed together and shopkeepers crowded their wares to the edges of the streets, leaving just enough room for the occasional horseman to get through. Latrines were only for the better houses; here, the streets, alleys and even open doorways were toilets. People flung their scraps out of the window and at night in the poorly lit streets could be heard the scurrying of rats. Leonardo stopped, thinking half aloud:

"Two levels. Streets running one above the other— one for pedestrians and one for carts and horses. Yes, and cutting through the whole city a system of canals to carry the city's waste to a river or to the sea. Why not

even ten cities of, say, five thousand houses in each—
say, no more than thirty thousand people to a city?"

Intent now on his thoughts he hurried to his home,
his mind busy with his visions of new cities.

During the years 1484 and 1485 the bubonic plague
swept Italy—the same dreaded Black Death so prevalent
in medieval times. Milan was one of the cities most
severely stricken. Every courtyard became a hospital
and the streets were deserted except for the rumbling
carts picking up the dead. On the roads from the city
were lines of refugees fleeing to the country. Surrounding cities that had not been infected manned their fortress walls as in wartime to keep the fleeing populations
out.

Ludovico at first tried to protect Milan from the
spread of the disease; then, frightened, he and his court
fled. Even the ruler's official documents had to be "dis-
infected" by perfume and then held for a period of
time before he would allow them near him.

Leonardo, sensing opportunity, drew out his plans for
his new cities. Canals running through them were to be
used for barges and the underground conduits greatly
resembled those of modern sewage systems. Paths were
to have gutters for the adequate drainage of the streets.
Public toilets were to be installed. Leonardo even had
plans for the control of smoke collecting over the city—
by sending it up tall chimneys where it was picked up
by fans and driven away over the roofs. The widths of
the streets were to be in proportion to the heights of the
houses—light and air would circulate freely. Two levels
would be connected by graceful ramps—the lower level

The results of the bubonic plague in Italy, 1484–85. Streets were deserted except for the carts picking up the dead.

for the commercial traffic and the upper level for the pedestrians. Where stairs were used they were designed so one could ascend or descend without one person seeing the other. Stables were devised so that animals were fed through openings in their mangers and under these were tunnels of flowing water for the removal of waste.

These sweeping plans Leonardo laid before Ludovico when the epidemic had subsided. But Ludovico, once his fear was overcome, brushed them aside as impossible dreams.

So Leonardo returned to the commission for the Fraternity and the designs for the bronze monument of Francesco Sforza. These jobs kept Leonardo from brooding about his rejections.

Often, too, Leonardo worked with Bernardino de Predis, the elder brother of Ambrogio. Bernardino was a minter of coins. As Leonardo watched him at the laborious task of first cutting disks from ingots and then hammering the design into the hot metal, he suggested to Bernardino an easier method, then used in Germany. This was to prepare smooth ribbons of metal of the desired thickness and with a punch, impress the design into the ribbon at the necessary intervals and then, punch out the coin. Leonardo went on to improve this system by designing precise punches for both faces of the coin. A single machine then cut out and stamped the coins, using a falling weight raised by little winches. This machine was later destined for the Vatican mint in Rome.

On March 26, 1485 an event occurred in Milan that was viewed with mingled fear, superstition, curiosity and excitement. There was a total eclipse of the sun. To some, coming as it did so soon after the plague, it was a judgment of God; to others, it was regarded as an omen—a sign for astrologers to use for predicting the future.

But to Leonardo the eclipse was a moment of great scientific importance. At this time in history, the Ptolemaic, or geocentric theory of the universe was the popular belief. This theory taught that the earth is fixed and the sun and moon revolve around it. Leonardo himself had believed this theory for a long time. As he grew older, however, he read and heard discussions of the heliocentric theory. This theory proposed that the sun is fixed and the earth and stars move around it. Now, as he watched the eclipse, his doubts of the Ptolemaic concept were renewed and he resolved to make experiments of his own. The new theory was so daring for his times, however, that it would be many years before he became convinced of its truth.

Later that night, deep in thought over the experience of the day, he noted down his observations of the eclipse and his doubts of the medieval concept of the heavens. The Church believed the earth was the fixed center of the universe. Scholars and scientists supported the belief of Aristotle in the four elements, earth, water, air, and fire—but something was wrong. What were the planets —what was the moon? He picked up his pen and on a clean sheet of paper he wrote, "Make glasses in order to see the moon large."

6

The

Monument

DURING this time, Leonardo had been struggling with the design for the bronze equestrian statue. Drawing after drawing lay scattered on his studio floor. Lately, however, a daring plan for this statue had come to him. It was to be a huge bronze warrior, Francesco Sforza, mounted on a rearing horse. Weighing perhaps a hundred thousand pounds, it was to be cast in sections in five furnaces—a fitting monument to the power of the Sforza family. But there still remained a big problem to be solved: how could he balance the plunging horse and man on just the two rear legs of the horse?

Meanwhile, Leonardo had another problem to work on—a wooden model of the Milan cathedral. He had entered his name with the cathedral authorities as a competitor in the design and construction of the cathedral's dome. Many architects had been brought in and had failed, partly because of the antagonism of the Milanese workmen to foreign craftsmen, and partly because the committee found it difficult to decide what designs it liked. Leonardo had sent them a letter outlining his own recommendations and had drawn many pages of possible plans. He put forward his knowledge of various building materials, his understanding of classical architecture, and his wish to keep his own ideas in harmony with the Gothic tradition of the cathedral itself. Often he would make a point of walking about the city, observing the different constructions under way and drawing up plans to shorten the labor by mechanical means.

In July of 1487 Leonardo received a payment from the cathedral authorities for the wooden model he had submitted. Still, however, no final decision had been reached. Now, as Leonardo looked at the model in his studio, he felt the urge to improve it further—to make it more perfect. Yet he held his impatience in check and decided he would wait a little longer. Instead, he decided to work on some of his ideas for construction devices. He had already made many drawings, but they could be improved, he thought, and he began to make calculations.

Among these notes and drawings was an improvement on a device for the raising of columns. It was a mobile windlass with a transmission gear for transporting and erecting columns and obelisks. Another device was an earth drill resembling a modern corkscrew with double handle bars. The upper bar, when turned, drilled the screw into the earth while the lower bar—when turned the opposite way—carried the dirt up and out. Also there was a double crane mounted on a circular trolley which carried the dirt of excavation up and then the crane was moved around on its trolley so the dirt could be unloaded in different directions.

Other labor-saving devices that Leonardo designed were an automatic pile driver, the weight of which was raised by a winch and tripped automatically at its height to fall on the piling; a lift for raising iron bells to bell towers; and a machine for boring tree trunks to make pipes for carrying water.

In the fall of 1488, Leonardo was interrupted by a summons from Ludovico, who wanted him to design and build the decorations for the forthcoming marriage of his nephew, young Duke Gian Galeazzo Sforza, to Isabella of Aragon, granddaughter of the King of Naples. He worked on this steadily until the wedding ceremony in February of the following year. When the day arrived, the street from the cathedral to the grim castle was trimmed with flags and banners of the two royal houses. The inner courtyards of the castle were transformed into delicate arbors of laurel boughs. Yet it was the evening's reception and entertainment which were to be the climax and to them Leonardo had brought all his mechanical skill. However, the announcement of the death of the bride's mother cut short the celebration and, after the bride and groom had left for Pavia, the wedding party soon dispersed. Disappointed that his decorations had not been fully appreciated, Leonardo returned to his studio and the problem of the monument.

He was still struggling with the problem of balancing the rearing horse. And, indeed, a solution was soon found. By placing a fallen soldier with his arm upraised in protection under the forefeet of the horse, Leonardo could balance the enormous weight and provide for the proper casting of the molten bronze.

Finally, Leonardo made a small wax model of the proposed statue and showed it to Ludovico. The nobleman was impressed by its originality. Most of the ideas contributed by other sculptors were mere variations of what had already been done many times. Also, the other plans called for bronze of not more than two thousand pounds, while Leonardo envisioned a statue fifty times that size! Ludovico awarded the commission to Leonardo.

Leonardo was to work on this commission for ten years and it was destined never to be immortalized in bronze, for reasons that will be explained later. His energies, as usual, were poured into many schemes. Growing out of his work on the monument he planned one book on the subject of casting in bronze and another on the anatomy of the horse. But the one subject, which he began to study in this period and which would occupy the remainder of his life, was the study of human anatomy. So Leonardo, in the midst of all his other activities, wrote in his notes, "On the second day of April 1489 the book entitled *Of the Human Figure*."

The sources of anatomical study up to Leonardo's day had been the Greeks—Hippocrates and Galen—

and the Arab—Avicenna. Books on this subject were few, and the anatomical diagrams were crude and inaccurate. Galen, for example, had based his studies on the dissection of monkeys. Renaissance anatomists had explained his errors by pointing out that man had probably changed since Galen's time. The Church had stepped in during the fourteenth century with an edict that was interpreted as a prohibition against dissection of the human body. In Italy, however, there were some dissections. They could only use, for this purpose, the bodies of criminals, slaves, and people of foreign birth. In Florence, anatomy was studied by the artists, and Leonardo had undoubtedly watched Pollaiuolo at work on a corpse that that artist had dissected.

In 1489 Leonardo, from the results of his own investigation, produced drawings of the skull and backbone whose careful attention to detail are—even today— classics in art and anatomy. With infinite patience and with a saw of his own invention he had halved a skull and drew for the first time with accuracy the curves of the frontal and sphenoid bones. He drew the lachrymal (tear) canal, and he was the first to show the cavity in the superior maxillary bone—not discovered again until 1651, by Highmore—now named "the antrum of Highmore." He was the first to demonstrate the double curvature of the spine and its accompanying vertebrae, the inclination of the sacrum, the shape of the rib cage, and the true position of the pelvis. He planned a whole series of books that would include from head to foot and from inside to outside every section of the human apparatus.

Meanwhile he had been working on the monument,

redesigning it to conform to the practical needs of casting. Now it had reached an even grander scale—a colossus that would require two hundred thousand pounds of bronze! He recorded in his notes the very day that this work was started, "On the twenty-third day of April 1490 I commenced this book and recommenced the horse." The "horse," of course, was the monument and "this book" referred to still another subject which had grown out of his studies of anatomy and perspective.

The title of the proposed book was to be *Light and Shade*. It would include the subject of optics or the mechanism of the eye, the problems of reflection and refraction and it would lead him eventually to a re-examination of his studies of the sun and moon.

In Leonardo's day, and even for a long while afterwards, the popular belief of vision was one that had originally been put forth by the Platonic school and expanded by Euclid and Ptolemy. This belief was that the eye sent forth rays that brought back the image to the soul. Leonardo, in his younger days, had believed in the same theory. Not content with what had been written on the subject, however, he began to experiment for himself.

These experiments led him to an examination of the eye itself. He noted the various parts of the eye—the optic foramen or opening, the pigment layer, and the iris. These were already known by the Arabs. Leonardo discovered, however, the crystalline area of the eye. He explained binocular vision, or three-dimensional images, by correctly noting the positions of the two eyes in the head. He described the variations in the diameter of the pupil according to the surrounding light. Further experiments with light brought him to the conclusion that light and images are received by the eye. He took a piece of paper, for example, and pierced it with a small hole. With this he looked at the source of light. He noted the cone shape of the rays funneling into the tiny hole and then when the paper was held next to a white wall he noted that the rays spread out again. He established that light travels in straight lines. He constructed the first "camera obscura"—a box with a small hole in

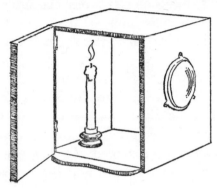

Leonardo's "camera obscura" which he used for projecting an image of an object on a wall or screen.

it. Inside the box an object was placed near the hole and behind that a lighted candle. When the box was closed the image of the object was cast on the wall. Leonardo was already acquainted with lenses, and he placed a magnifying lens over the hole to create an enlarged image.

He also demonstrated various laws relative to optical illusion, such as irradiation—when a metal rod is made red-hot at one end, that end seems thicker than the other. A brightly lit object seems larger than one exactly like it that is dimly lit; a dark object placed against a light background seems smaller than it is; a light object seems larger than its real size when placed against a dark background; and the illusion of a light swung in a circle appears as a complete circle of light.

Many years before Newton, Leonardo described the experiment of breaking up a ray of white light into the solar spectrum. Also he compared two sources of light and measured their intensity by the depth of their shadows accompanied by a drawing that was the forerunner of Rumford's photometer three centuries later! He stated the law of reflection—that is, that the angle of reflection is always equal to the angle of incidence.

About this time Leonardo left the studio of Ambrogio de Predis and moved into the Sforza Castle. Ludovico had put at his disposal a studio in the Corte Vecchia and the use of a room in one of the towers—which Leonardo always kept locked. To his growing list of work, Leonardo now had to add the preparations for the delayed wedding reception of Ludovico's nephew, Gian Galeazzo Sforza.

On a cold winter evening of January 1490 the guests assembled again. Silks, satins and gold brocade, diamonds, rubies and pearls glittered in the brilliant lights. Princes of the Church mingled with ambassadors of foreign lands. Music and perfume filled the air and as the party quieted down the entertainment began. There were dances in gay costumes. Poetry was recited that flattered the bride and groom. There were allegorical processions. The jokes and antics of the court jester made the audience laugh.

Then, at midnight, the curtain that hung from wall

to wall at the end of the ballroom was raised. Applause and cries of delight greeted the spectacle. The rising curtain revealed a room in which there was a hemisphere surrounded by the signs of the zodiac and the planets. While the planets in their niches flickered with concealed lights and the signs of the zodiac glowed, lines were spoken in honor of the house of Sforza to the accompaniment of a choir. The ancient gods swept down from the heavens, and the Virtues and Graces moved across the scene with nymphs waving lanterns. The music drowned out the sound of the mechanism. This was the kind of mechanics that Ludovico could understand and appreciate.

The success of this entertainment so pleased Ludovico that Leonardo was encouraged to present another amusing idea. This one was an "alarm clock" and it utilized what we call today the mechanical relay principle. When a small power is suddenly switched over, the power is reinforced. The "alarm" clock worked by placing a shallow basin of water at one end of a tubed lever. At the other end was another empty basin. Water was led drop by drop into the second basin and as this slowly filled the increasing weight lowered the lever. The shallow basin of water at the first end was suddenly emptied and the immediate switch in weight flipped the lever up and this in turn pushed up the sleeper's feet.

Leonardo decided to withdraw from the competition for the cathedral dome. Although the cathedral authorities were pleased with his design, they could not decide to whom the commission should be awarded. In the summer of 1490 Ludovico was called upon to settle the issue and he decided in favor of Antonio Amadeo from Milan. But the work that Leonardo had done so impressed Ludovico that he sent him to Pavia in company with an architect from Siena, Francesco di Giorgio Martini, to inspect the work on the cathedral of that city. Leonardo, who had his own workshop and apprentices now, took along one of them, Marco d'Oggionno, a young boy of twenty.

In Pavia one of the greatest libraries in all of Italy was in the ducal palace. Here Leonardo wandered among shelves of books and illuminated manuscripts bound in rich velvets and gold-embossed leather all bound to their places with silver chains. One book that he records in his notes was written in the thirteenth century by Witelo, a Polish scholar, who wrote extensively on perspective. Leonardo, by the necessity of his art, had solved many problems in perspective. He had invented a pair of proportional compasses, the forerunners of those used today for the transfer of a drawing from one scale to duplicate the same drawing in a larger scale. Leonardo had also designed in very careful detail a parabolic compass for drawing a parabola in one continuous movement. He now determined to write his own book on perspective and, as the subject was so close to his studies of the eye, he would entitle it *Introduction to Perspective, or the Function of the Eye.*

Leonardo submitted a number of plans for the completion of the cathedral to the authorities in Pavia and then returned to Milan. He worked through the rest of the summer on the equestrian statue and at the same time he continued to expand his notes on anatomy, light and shade, and perspective.

Late on a cold December night in 1490, Leonardo lit his lamp. This was a very special lamp that he had invented. It had already created a great deal of comment. It was so unusual, he had received an order from the court for another which he made with a richly carved pedestal. Candles, torches, and oil lamps, the only methods of artificial illumination in those days, were poor substitutes for light. They flickered, smoked, went out, and frequently caused damage with their hot drippings. As a side result of his experiments in light, Leonardo had put a glass cylinder in the middle of a larger glass globe. A wick in olive oil was placed in the cylinder and the outside globe was then filled with water. The result was a bright, steady light magnified by the water in the globe.

He sat down by the small fire and arranged his papers in front of him. Then, with a glance at his lamp, he picked up his goose-quill pen and wrote, "No substance can be comprehended without light and shade; light and shade are caused by light."

7

Success

It was January of 1491, and a light snow had fallen in Milan, edging with white all the roofs, the massive spires of the cathedral and the red battlements of the Sforza castle. Soon Ludovico was to be married to Beatrice d'Este of the ducal house of Ferrara.

Once more the streets of Milan echoed to the carpenters' hammers. Messengers rode to and from the castle and endless carts full of provisions pushed through the crowded city. Guests began to arrive from all the allied courts of Italy with their bodyguards and servants. The rooms of the castle, the palaces of the nobles, and even the inns were filling with the royal processions.

Leonardo was again summoned by the court to prepare the decorations, the costumes for the masquerades, and the arena for the jousting tournaments. An invitation had been sent to all the friendly courts to attend these contests-at-arms. So, accompanying each new party's arrival was a band of armored knights, their breast-plates, helmets, and shields glistening in the winter sun.

Leonardo enjoyed designing mechanical toys and entertaining the guests with them. One of these was a mechanical drum. Ordinarily most of the entertainment began with normal drum rolls, but Leonardo's rolls were made on a kind of wheelbarrow. On it was mounted an enormous drum. When the "wheelbarrow" was pushed, it put into motion a cogged wheel geared to the axle. This wheel in turn was geared to two rotary cylinders with pegs mounted around the top. The pegs moved against five drumsticks on either side of the drum and thumped out a rhythm according to the position of the pegs.

Ludovico's marriage to Beatrice d'Este, a girl of little more than fifteen years, further isolated Leonardo from the court. Being almost a child, Beatrice loved parties and festivities, and she surrounded herself with people who catered to her frivolous whims. As a result so serious a man as Leonardo was forced into the background of the court life. He was called upon more and more to act as stage-designer while his more important work went unnoticed. Because these entertainments were easy for Leonardo to design, they did give him more time to work on his giant equestrian monument of Francesco Sforza. Working one day on the scaffolding surrounding the clay figure of his statue, Leonardo heard a knock at his studio door.

"Come in," he shouted as he climbed down. "The door's open."

Three peasants cautiously entered the room and quickly took off their caps. One of them was holding a carefully wrapped bundle.

"Master Leonardo, we have brought you some shells we found on a ridge of Monferrato. Remember, you asked us to bring anything we found that was unusual?"

"Yes, Pietro. Thank you. Put them here on the table."

Leonardo opened the bundle. He smiled when he saw the shells. He remembered how, as a young boy, he had found seashells like these high in the mountains. Leonardo questioned Pietro and his companions as to where they had been found and under what circumstances. He gave them some coins and, when they had gone, he looked among his growing collection of notes and drawings on the shelves. It took some time for him to find what he wanted, for the pages were in such confusion. Finally, he sat down at the table with several of the sheets and, putting the seashells in front of him, he began to make notes.

The shells were fossil shells but, thought Leonardo, their presence on the high mountains of Lombardy could hardly be attributed to the great flood as described in the Bible. In his notes, Leonardo cited the case of the cockle which, out of water, is like the snail. It makes a furrow in the sand and can travel in this furrow about three to four yards a day. By such means, he calculated, it could not possibly have reached Monferrato from the Adriatic in forty days (which was supposed to have been the duration of the flood)—a distance of 250 miles. Nor were these simply dead shells deposited by the waves—for the living creatures are recognized by being in pairs, and these in front of him had certainly been traveling in pairs. Consequently, they could have been left there only when they were alive and the mountains were covered by the primeval oceans. Moreover, Leonardo also described how living matter in prehistoric times fell into the mud and died, and how this mud, as the waters receded and years had passed, was changed into rock forming a mold about the fossil— literally making a cast of its original living appearance.

By such deductive reasoning and the testing of the evidence before him against the common beliefs, Leonardo struggled to free the minds of men from medieval superstitions and beliefs. Indeed, these medieval superstitions existed everywhere. Astrologers, or men who told fortunes by the position of the stars at a given moment; and necromancers, those who by tricks of magic claimed to be able to talk to departed spirits—these men profited from the ignorant. The Church, with its preaching of devils and hells, provided the background against which these fakers flourished.

Ludovico Sforza was himself a believer in such things. His own physician and astrologer was a man by the name of Ambrogio da Rosate, who had such influence over the court that he was given a post in the University of Pavia, and his fame was so great that he was called upon to predict the future of Pope Innocent VIII! Leonardo's dislike of these men was intense. He scorned the supernatural and asked men to look about them at the real world and the real heavens. Observation and experiment—these were Leonardo's key words. But he was a lonely figure in his thinking—like a man awake while the rest of the world slept.

At last the full-size model of the Sforza monument was nearing completion. Ludovico had ordered it ready for exhibition in the courtyard of the castle for yet another marriage festival that was soon to take place. This time it was the marriage of his niece Bianca Maria to Maximilian I of Germany. Leonardo and his assistants were busy with the finishing touches on the monument, and with building a wagon on which to carry it from the studio to the courtyard.

During these last months Leonardo had had to struggle with all kinds of heavy loads. Already he had improved on pulleys by inventing a new kind of tackle, and he also had utilized many kinds of levers. One of his simpler discoveries for raising heavy weights was a jack which, in appearance and principle, was the forerunner of our own automobile jack.

In 1493 when the clay model of the Sforza monument was completed, it was put on the cart and wheeled to its place of exhibition where a curtain was thrown around it. Again Milan was the host to a gathering of noble courts, and this time Ludovico outdid himself in the display of luxury. Tapestries hung from the buildings and rich carpets were laid down the steps of the cathedral. Everything that Milan had to show was on exhibition—even a crocodile.

But the most impressive sight of all was the unveiling of Leonardo's colossal statue. It rose in majesty against the red walls of the castle. The name of Leonardo da Vinci was suddenly on everyone's lips. As the word of his artistic achievement spread from city to city, messages of praise came pouring in. And, for a while the years of frustration and failure to gain recognition melted away. Leonardo at forty-one had at last achieved some success.

Now there was a breathing spell, and Leonardo returned to some of his own projects. For a long time he had continued his observations of his two favorite elements—air and water. To him they were related in their movements. The birds flying in the currents of air and the fish swimming in the flow of water seemed very similar to him. He had already designed various instruments to tell him about the direction of wind and its velocity, and he had also commenced to analyze the wing structure of birds and bats. To soar through the air like a bird was an ancient dream of man, yet for Leonardo it had become a passion. Ceaselessly, he sketched the flights of birds, the flutterings of butterflies and analyzed their flying patterns.

But to Leonardo, understanding the *dynamics*, or motion, of air was the most important thing. He built an *anemoscope*, an instrument like a weather-vane for telling the direction of the wind; and, he also constructed several types of *anemometers* for measuring the velocity or force of the wind. One of these latter consisted of a thin rectangle of metal hanging straight down in front of an upward-curving wooden arc. This arc was marked off in units of measurement. When the wind blew, it pushed the thin rectangle up the arc; thus, by noting at which gradation it stopped, Leonardo could tell the velocity.

In addition, Leonardo at this time constructed a de-

*One of Leonardo's anemometers. The wind blew against
the strip of metal, pushing it up the curved gauge and
thereby measuring the force of the wind.*

vice which has been compared to the modern instrument used for testing the weight-carrying capacity of
airplane wings. He fashioned a wing resembling a bird's
wing and attached it to a lever so that it would be possible to lower the wing by pushing rapidly down on the
lever. This wing in turn was mounted on a plank that
was in weight equal to that of a human being. He then
calculated that two wings of this kind would have to be
about twelve meters wide and twelve meters long to
raise a man and his machine together. Another device
resembling those found in airplanes today that Leonardo
constructed was an inclination gauge. He made this by
suspending a heavy ball on a cord within a glass bell.
This ball was then supposed to guide the flyer by telling
him whether he was flying level, diagonally, up, or
down.

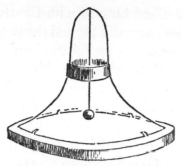

Leonardo's inclination gauge, designed to guide a man in flight. The ball in the glass cylinder was supposed to tell a "flyer" whether or not he was flying level or tipped.

To Leonardo, water was also a phenomenon that from his youth never failed to excite his curiosity. The use of water power to run machines, to irrigate fields and to carry boats inland was a subject that he never ceased investigating. Out of his experiments at this time he constructed a device for raising water to high levels. It was based on the geometric spiral of Archimedes. He took a piece of gut, inflated it, and let it dry. Then, covering it with a coat of wax to make it waterproof, he wound it around a thin staff in a spiral. He put one end in a stream and attached it by gears to a cogged water wheel; this set the long screw to turning, and he was able to raise water from a low level to any height he desired. With a multiple system of these screws he could raise water in continuous circulation to the reservoirs on the highest towers.

In the year 1494, King Charles VIII of France crossed the Alps at the head of an army of twenty-five thousand men. Now Ludovico, by a series of diplomatic maneuvers, had allied himself with Charles and had, by secret negotiation, actually invited the invasion. By such an alliance he hoped to use Charles' army to overcome the forces of the Pope which stood in the path of Ludovico's ambition to become the most powerful ruler in Italy. Outwardly Charles was asserting his rights to the Kingdom of Naples, but inwardly he dreamt of leading a crusade against the infidels in the Holy Land. At the same time young Gian Galeazzo Sforza, Duke of Milan, was dying. Ludovico desired this title for himself; however, until Galeazzo was out of the way, he could not have it. There were ugly rumors that young Sforza had been poisoned. Moreover, in 1494, the Medicis—another powerful obstacle—were expelled from Florence, and a republic was established.

Soon young Gian Galeazzo died, leaving a son, Francesco. This son was the rightful heir to the Dukedom of Milan but Ludovico usurped the boy's claim and declared himself Duke of Milan. Now Ludovico was in a position to await the impending battle between Charles and the Pope.

With such military and political ambitions in mind, Duke Ludovico now assigned Leonardo the task of reviewing Milan's defenses. Again Leonardo submitted to Ludovico his plans for strengthening fortresses and designs for new ones. The great architect Bramante was also assigned the task of seeing to the city's defenses, and for some time the two brilliant men worked together.

Then, in the spring of 1494, Leonardo was sent to Vigevano where Ludovico's young wife was staying. This town was also the birthplace of Ludovico, and

Leonardo was given the job of designing and building a small summer house and garden there for Beatrice. In addition, Leonardo built a kind of "air conditioner" for her bedroom. In consisted of a large waterwheel that cooled the air circulated into her room. Although this ancient device had long been known to the Greeks and Romans, Leonardo was the one who succeeded in perfecting it.

During this time Leonardo's highly original mind was also at work on other devices. One of these was an *odometer*, an instrument for measuring the distance traversed by a vehicle. Dials, turned by a system of gears attached to the wheel of a wheelbarrow, measured the distance traveled as the barrow was pushed along the ground. In addition, Leonardo conceived a kind of odometer to be used at sea; this consisted essentially of a spinner that was towed by a ship which registered its speed. Leonardo even invented an automatic spit operated by metal vanes mounted in the chimney that revolved with the pressure of the hot air rising from the fire—and a pair of large floating shoes for walking on water!

In the meantime, Charles VIII of France had marched through Rome and entered Naples. The conquest was without opposition. Charles was then crowned King of Naples and all Italy was at his feet. Yet his triumph was a short one. Ludovico, having used the king to get rid of his enemies, now plotted against the king himself. He formed an alliance with the Pope, Venice, Spain, and the German emperor. Charles, faced with this league, hastily beat a retreat to France. Fighting his way to the border, he there signed a peace treaty. Thus Ludovico had swept Italy clean of all opposition and was now the most powerful prince in the land.

Yet Ludovico was quick to realize that his position could only be held by force and he set about strengthening himself and his allies. To provide for more cannons, a hundred and fifty thousand tons of bronze were sent to manufacturing works in Ferrara. This, however, included the very bronze Leonardo needed for the casting of his equestrian statue, and this is why the statue was never cast. Years of Leonardo's work now seemed to vanish overnight. Ludovico also needed large sums of money to secure friends in high places and Leonardo's own payments were suddenly dropped. Forced again to worry about paying for his daily bread and for his household and apprentices, he wrote letters to Ludovico complaining of his lack of funds and asking for money that was owed him for work done. He looked about for other commissions, but none were available. Moreover, because he was still court painter to Ludovico, he was ordered to paint the decorations of some rooms in the castle. But this was more than Leonardo could take—he walked off the job without finishing it.

Despite all of these misfortunes, Leonardo continued struggling with the problems of flight. He kept working out the proportions of wing span to the weight of the load. Indeed, he had already started designs for a flying machine. He had chosen a room which was the highest in one of the towers of the castle and which had access to a roof. Leonardo's plans for a flying machine were a secret, and, with the exception of an assistant, no one knew about them. He made sure that he could not be seen by the workmen on the dome of the cathedral and proceeded to block off his room with beams which he planned to use as supports for his model.

He had thought at first that any attempted flight should take place over water in order to cushion a possible crash—but as his plans progressed he designed a parachute. It was a pyramid-shaped "tent of linen" twenty-four feet broad and twenty-four feet high, and it is believed to have been successfully tried out from a tower especially constructed for that purpose.

Since Leonardo was no longer working for Ludovico, he lived more simply than ever. He made regular lists of his expenses down to the last penny. His habits were frugal although he always kept himself neat. His meals were spare; he drank a little wine at meals and never ate meat. To his pupils and apprentices, he recommended regular habits such as not sleeping during midday, eating only when hungry and chewing well, exercising moderately, and sleeping well covered.

Yet, even though Leonardo lived cheaply, he was now greatly in need of money. Swallowing his pride, he wrote to Ludovico, placing himself at the duke's service once again. His absence from court, he said, had been necessary so that he could earn a living. In this and other ways, Leonardo attempted to heal the break between them.

It turned out that Ludovico was glad to have Leonardo back. Perhaps mindful of the fame that the model of the equestrian monument had brought the house of Sforza, he now commissioned Leonardo to paint a picture. The Dominican monastery of Santa Maria delle Grazie was the nearest church to the Sforza castle and a favorite retreat of Ludovico. Here he used to walk in the quiet garden while the white-robed monks silently went about their chores. In gratitude for the peace he found there, Ludovico had had the refectory rebuilt and on, the back wall, a crucifixion scene had been painted by Montorfano, a Lombard. But the front wall was given to Leonardo. On this Leonardo decided to paint a picture of the Last Supper—the painting that has since become one of the best known in the world.

8

The

French

THE noonday sun was baking the deserted streets of Milan as Leonardo hurried across the drawbridge of the castle. The guard dozing in the entrance arch started to his feet, but when he saw who it was he sat down again, muttering about a madman. Taking the shortest way, Leonardo arrived at the monastery gate and pulled on the bellcord. When the gate opened Leonardo brushed past the startled monk and made directly for the scaffolding in the refectory. He looked at his almost completed painting for a moment, took a brush and mixed a color swiftly on the large palette. Then he climbed the scaffolding and very quickly applied three or four strokes. With this he sighed and smiled. Then, just as abruptly, he put away his brushes and, without a backward glance, he left, making his way back to the castle in the hot sun.

For three years, Leonardo had been working this way on the "Last Supper."

Sometimes he would work from dawn to dusk forgetting to eat; other times, he would stay away for days and then run back just to add a touch. Once he arrived and, with his arms folded across his chest, he stood in front of it for two hours just studying what he had done.

Now, in 1498, the painting was nearing completion and the only faces still left blank were those of Christ and Judas. Leonardo had drawn hundreds of sketches, taking his models wherever he found them—once he sketched a man just for his hands. Now that his name had become well known he always had an audience while he worked. His pupils, the monks, visiting nobility, church officials, and frequently Ludovico himself watched him as he painted the "Last Supper."

But Leonardo, as usual, was involved in many different tasks. He was supervising the installation of a hydraulic pump over seventy feet high beside a stream which would use the power of the stream itself to pump water into the castle. Mindful, too, of the uncertainty of court patronage, he was designing commercial machinery, hoping thereby to secure an income outside the court. Among the most notable of these were an olive press, an automatic file-cutter, a hydraulic saw, and a needle sharpener. This latter was a forerunner of modern sharpeners with their mass-production methods. With it, Leonardo dreamt of sharpening four hundred needles at a time, or forty thousand an hour so that in twelve hours one person could sharpen four hundred and eighty thousand needles! The needles were arranged successively on a moving belt of leather and brought against a rotating grindstone. This grindstone was set in such a way that the needles were sharpened into curvilinear points rather than the usual triangular points.

In his travels to Vigevano and other parts of the countryside around Milan, Leonardo had studied flour mills. He had talked with the workmen, asked the prices of grain, and noted the time that it took to do the milling. Then he made calculations on ways to cut down the time, and, in fact, redesigned the entire mill. He mounted twelve cylindrical millstones in rows of four on one side of a canal and another twelve on the other side. In the canal were hydraulic wheels or paddlewheels. Each wheel was attached to a rod that ran underneath four millstones. Geared to the one rod were four grinding levers to the stones above. In this way it was possible to have twenty-four millstones operating at the same time.

But most fascinating to Leonardo now was the construction of his flying machine. His first models involved the principle of an air-screw mounted on a platform on which a man stood. But where would the necessary power come from to lift his machine from the ground? At first he thought of operating his air-screw by means of a steel spring coiled around a drum, but this he apparently abandoned. Later, however, Leonardo did design another model on this principle which has been called the forerunner of the modern helicopter. It was to be operated by four men standing on a platform. Each man would hold a bar which wound a spring-driven mechanism, much as in a modern clockworks. The air-screw was a broad blade spiraling about a vertical shaft—the ancestor of the modern propeller.

The model that Leonardo wanted to construct now, however, was of a different principle. Instead of an air-screw he substituted a pair of wings fashioned after those of the birds. There was still a platform on which the flyer stood and two springs were still the essential "motor" to raise and lower the wings. But as Leonardo worked on his apparatus he began to realize that it would be too much at the mercy of a sudden gust of wind or a violent updraft. It was necessary to return to his study of the air and its currents.

With all of this activity in mechanical devices Leonardo had reawakened his interest in mathematics. During this time he was introduced to a man at Ludovico's court who became his friend and collaborator. He was a Franciscan monk named Fra Luca Pacioli who had been appointed a professor of mathematics by Ludovico. He, too, came from Florence, and in 1496, when he met Leonardo, he was forty-six years old and the author of *Summa di Arithmetica*, the first printed scientific work of his time. Pacioli was now at work on a book of geometry to be entitled *De Divina Proportione* and he enlisted Leonardo's aid in drawing the plates for his book. As Leonardo had already made a study of human proportions, the association with Pacioli was of benefit to them both. Among Leonardo's best known drawings of human proportion is a beautifully rendered figure-study of a standing man with his arms at his sides and then outstretched, his legs together and then apart, inscribed within a square and a circle. It was made to illustrate a passage from Vitruvius on the proportions of a human figure and demonstrated, among other things, "the span of a man's outstretched arms is equal to his height."

Moreover, Leonardo found with Pacioli confirmation of many of his own observations and experiments and in turn Pacioli gave to Leonardo a confidence in his own methods. Pacioli also helped Leonardo with his arithmetic, a subject that Leonardo had neglected in his impatience to study geometry. The association also helped to free him further from the cobwebs of medieval beliefs. For Pacioli, the friendship with Leonardo was a revelation. Although Pacioli was a learned mathematician, Leonardo demonstrated to him that the application of his science encompassed *all* sciences—even art—for Leonardo later wrote, "Let no one read me who is not a mathematician . . ."

Legend relates that Leonardo became so absorbed in his studies that the prior of the monastery complained to Ludovico that the "Last Supper," although nearly completed, still lacked the faces of Christ and Judas. Ludovico summoned Leonardo to court and laid the complaint before him. Leonardo, however, was quick to reply.

"The good prior is an esteemed man, your Grace, but he is a monk-and not a painter. Little does he know that I spend at least two hours a day on my painting."

"But Master, he says he never sees you there, so how do you explain these two hours a day?"

"Excellency, the figure of Judas must be of incomparable evil. Every day I search for this face in the criminal quarter, and every day I fail to find the evil that I am looking for. If I cannot find this man, however, I can use the head of the prior—it would do admirably, but I have hesitated for fear of hurting his feelings."

Ludovico slapped his knees and roared with laughter. There were no more complaints.

Finally, in 1498, the scaffolding was removed from the painting and Leonardo's masterpiece was revealed. The twelve apostles grouped at the table are shown each responding in his own way to the words of Christ, "One of you shall betray me." Again hundreds flocked to see this latest marvel of Leonardo's. Its striking influence was felt by generations of painters. Even now, more than four hundred and fifty years later, the world still comes to stand before the genius of Leonardo da Vinci in the refectory of Santa Maria delle Grazie.

The clouds of war were gathering again over Italy. In April of 1498, Charles VIII of France died and his successor was Louis of Orleans, who became Louis XII. The new King of France laid claim to the Dukedom of Milan, and Ludovico again tried to form an alliance against him. But the years of juggling enemy against enemy and friend against friend were now coming to an end. No one trusted Il Moro any more, and suddenly he realized that he was to be alone in this new fight. After nearly twenty years of power sustained by powerful alliances, Ludovico was forced to turn to his own people of Lombardy.

Frantically he tried to correct the injustices of years. The people had been cruelly taxed to support the extravagances of the Sforza court, and, in addition, they had been badly treated by petty government officials. Ludovico now sought to repay the past miseries of his people and to rally them to his support. In such a spirit he remembered his court painter, Leonardo da Vinci, and gave him a vineyard and considerable piece of land not far from the Porta Vercellina.

Now, for the first time in his life, Leonardo knew financial security. With the income from the vineyard, and in the peace of his estate, he was left free to follow his own researches. He took no notice that his "peace" was surrounded by the threat of war. Indeed, he remained aloof from politics and court intrigues as much as was possible for a man living in the midst of such chaotic times.

Leonardo now had the opportunity to follow up an early interest—the study of plants. He made many beautiful drawings; no plant was too small to catch his eye. His notes on botany began to grow. With his genius for observation and analysis of nature, Leonardo made some extraordinary discoveries of botanical laws entirely unknown before his time. He wrote of the phenomenon of *heliotropism*, or the movement of plants toward or away from the sunlight. In addition, he described the phenomenon known as *geotropism*, or the growth of plants according to gravitational law, as for example, roots growing downward and shoots growing upward. He also defined the laws of phyllotaxis, which describe the system or order of leaf arrangement on a plant's stem. That is, leaves are arranged spirally around a stem so that the third leaf above grows out over the third leaf below on one type of plant; or, on another type, the two third leaves are over the two third leaves below. The same natural laws apply to the branches of plants as well; they occur so that every leaf and branch can receive sufficient air and light. Amazingly enough, these laws, which Leonardo described so completely, were not rediscovered until almost two centuries later!

Leonardo went even further in his botanical studies. He experimented with gourds, planting them in various aqueous solutions; this anticipated modern methods of growing plants in chemicals. He also tested the actions of arsenic and mercury poisons in plants. He reproduced the shape and form of leaves by pressing them on paper coated with lampblack, a method that was not used again until the nineteenth century. Carefully noted, too, in his writings was the rising of sap from the roots to the branches by capillary action; this, too, was not rediscovered until much later—in the eighteenth century. Leonardo also extracted oils and essences from flowers and studied the influences of altitude on the development of vegetation. Indeed Leonardo's very approaches to a systematic classification of plants were the forerunners of modern methods of classifying.

In the seclusion of his own home, as he continued his studies of geometry with Pacioli, Leonardo again turned to his observations of the heavens. On the roof of his house he had set up a small observatory for watching the sky at night. Often he looked at the stars through a pinhole in a sheet of paper. Leonardo did this to stop the "twinkling" of the stars which he recognized as an optical illusion. Moreover, by looking at the stars in this manner, he noticed that some were larger than others, and imagined to himself how our own earth might look from them. Would we not be but another "star" in a vast collection of stars? And if that were true—how could the earth be the center of the universe? By the same imaginary reasoning, he speculated on how we must look to someone on the moon. Realizing that the moonlight on earth faintly illuminates the dark side of the earth, he reasoned that then there must be an "earthlight" doing the same on the moon. Thus he was the first to explain the dim reflected light on the dark side of the moon. Moreover, Leonardo is known to have looked at the moon through a convex lens, and perhaps even a form of telescope. Indeed, he had built telescopic-type tubes with lenses in them and had written directions for their use. It seems certain that at about this time Leonardo became convinced of the heliocentric theory, the theory that states the sun is the center of our universe. On a sheet of mathematical notes Leonardo wrote in large letters, "the sun does not move."

During this time he continued to seek out books on astronomy. Leonardo was familiar with Aristotle's *Meteorology*, Archimedes' *On the Center of Gravity*, and with *Problems in Aristotle's Books of the Sky and the World*, a work by Albert of Saxony. This last book Leonardo had to read with the help of a Latin dictionary, because his Latin was not good. He had already read Plutarch, who had defined the moon as a solid. Plutarch had written further that the "spots" on the moon were the result of shadows cast by irregularities on its surface. This theory, that was apparently abandoned during the Middle Ages, supported the conclusions that Leonardo had reached by his own observations. But he still struggled against a mistaken idea of his own. For a long while he maintained that there were seas and waters upon the moon which accounted for the sunlight being reflected so brilliantly.

Meanwhile, in July of 1499, the French army had reached Lombardy. Ludovico was now in a state of desperation. He tried to appeal to the people of Milan, explaining that their heavy taxes had been due to the constant threats from abroad. But, however hard he tried to arouse their sense of loyalty to him, the public of Milan turned a deaf ear. They had not forgotten how Ludovico had allied himself with Charles VIII—a foreign king! Ludovico now had to put his trust in his army commander, Galeazzo da Sanseverino, despite warnings that this was a man of doubtful loyalty. Moreover, to make matters worse, Louis XII had succeeded in forming an alliance against Ludovico; and, among his allies was a powerful cardinal, son of Pope Alexander VI—the notorious Cesare Borgia.

From a note on a page of designs for supplying and heating a bath we know that Leonardo continued his quiet life, only vaguely disturbed by the political upheaval taking place around him. His note reads, "On the first day of August 1499 I wrote here of movement and weight." He had made many experiments and calculations concerning the movement and weight of objects. He had drawn, for example, the flight of an arrow to describe motion through air and although he wrote no specific formula, he marked the three stages of its trajectory—the initial push, the slowing and the steeper downward path as the arrow's momentum was overcome by the resistance of the air. He also defined the law of movement on an inclined plane and he arrived at the root principle of Newton's law of gravitation when he wrote, "every weight tends to fall toward the center by the shortest way."

A diagram of this period is probably the first scientific graph. Leonardo had experimented with two balls dropped from a height. First he dropped them together and then one after the other. In attempting to solve the mathematical problems presented by these falling bodies he drew a graph of vertical and horizontal lines. The times it took for the balls to fall were marked on the horizontal lines and the distances on the vertical lines— thus, he could trace their relationship.

But this peaceful time of productive work was running out for Leonardo. Ludovico's commander, Galeazzo, had yielded the fortress of Alessandria to the French at the first battle. Ludovico himself had sent his sons and his treasure to his brother, Cardinal Ascanio, in Germany. When he saw that his cause was lost, he turned the Sforza castle over to Bernardino da Corte, a trusted commander, making certain that it was fully supplied with arms and food. Then in sorrow, Ludovico Sforza, Duke of Milan, left his city for the last time as ruler of Lombardy. The gates of Milan were opened to the French in October of 1499, and Bernardino da Corte surrendered the Sforza castle.

French soldiers now occupied Milan as conquerors and the people of the city were in a state of confusion. Those who could made their peace with the French; but others, who had been supporters of Ludovico, fled to avoid arrest. Leonardo, who would be suspect to the French, packed up his few possessions—although he did manage to retain his estate—and left, together with Pacioli and an apprentice, for Mantua.

Leonardo had to flee Milan.

9

Cesare
Borgia

LEONARDO, Pacioli, and Salai, the apprentice, arrived in
Mantua in February of the year 1500. They were given
refuge in the castle of Isabella d'Este, who was the sister
of Beatrice, and the wife of Francesco Gonzaga, governor of Mantua. Isabella was one of the eminent women
of her time and attracted to her court the intellectual
life of Italy. In Leonardo she recognized the man of
genius; indeed, she treated him as an equal, putting her
castle at his disposal. She persuaded him to paint her

portrait and Leonardo commenced a preparatory drawing.

In the evenings at the castle there were discussions and
music and here Leonardo again met his pupil and companion on the trip from Florence so many years ago—
Atalante Migliorotti who had left Milan in 1490 to
assume the post of court musician to Isabella.

Although Leonardo had found a haven of peace in the
political storm that raged about the city state of Mantua,
he and Pacioli took to the road again for reasons unknown. Isabella d'Este, who still wanted Leonardo at
her court, sent many a letter and messenger in the following years to bring Leonardo back—first to finish the
portrait and then, when that failed, to sell to her any
picture that Leonardo wished to send. Strangely enough,
however, Leonardo seems to have turned his back upon
the one sympathetic person he had met in a world of
indifference.

The first, warm breezes of spring were blowing over
the lagoons of Venice when Leonardo and Pacioli
stepped ashore on the Piazzetta, or Little Square of San
Marco. But the beauty of this jewel-like city rising from
the sea was momentarily ignored by the two travelers
for an angry, frightened crowd had gathered about the
Doge's palace on the Piazzetta.

The people of Venice were fearful because their fleet
had just suffered a crushing defeat by the Turks. This
meant that their power at sea, once supreme, was now no
more. Year by year, moreover, their possessions in the
east had been slowly whittled away, and now the city
itself was threatened by invasion. At this same time, the

Venetian ambassador, Manenti, hoping to make peace
with the Turks, had been rudely rejected by them. Panic
soon swept the city and rumors of the bloodthirsty in-
fidel passed from person to person like the rush of an
ugly wind. Barricades were put up and windows were
barred. In this charged atmosphere, Leonardo and
Pacioli sought out their lodgings.

Soon after Leonardo's arrival here—either because
his reputation had preceded him or, more likely, because
of Fra Luca Pacioli's recommendations—he became
directly involved with the defenses of Venice. Immedi-
dately he was sent on an inspection trip of the city's
existing defenses, especially those inland from where an
invasion would probably come. When he had seen
them, he recommended a system of defenses along the
Isonzo river near the present border of Yugoslavia, using
the river itself to the disadvantage of the enemy. He
also made suggestions for the improvement of forts, and
even drew up plans for a completely new type—a circular fort. This consisted of a central, circular fort surrounded by two belts of fortresses each separated by a
moat. In the outside moat were four semicircular out-
posts. Communication was by underground galleries.
The total absence of superstructure and projecting bal-
conies was a new idea for the times. Another new defense idea was to station in the moat itself a low, thick
tower almost completely submerged, defended by a thin
opening near the waterline. It was reached from the
main fort by an underground passage and the gunsmoke
was removed by vents. According to Leonardo no enemy could conceal himself in any part of the defenses
and not be seen from such an outpost.

Leonardo's most unusual scheme for defending Venice, however, was his idea of approaching an enemy fleet under the water and then putting holes in the hulls of their ships. Actually, the idea of diving was not a new one. Aristotle had written of diving and diving bells, and certainly the stories of pearl fishers in the Orient were well known in the Renaissance. But Leonardo designed a diver's suit closely resembling those used today. This consisted of a complete suit of leather with helmet and eyepieces; it was made airtight by spirals of steel at the joints. He then added a bladder for holding air which fastened inside the suit at the diver's chest. It is possible that Leonardo also invented an air chamber that could be used by the diver while under water—but he was very secretive about this invention for fear of how men might abuse such a discovery. He wrote, ". . . and this I do not publish or divulge, on account of the evil nature of man, who would practice assassinations at the bottom of the seas . . ."

Leonardo felt the same way about a "submarine" that he presented to the Councilors and Tribunal of Venice. This resembled a turtle's shell with a raised bump on the center which was the "periscope." When submerged the water probably rose to an area just around the "periscope," but, again, the information about its air-supply is missing and the only reference to it is a reminder to close the "l—." In addition, he invented a system of screws mounted in tongs with the borer in the middle for putting holes in the bottoms of enemy ships, and at the same time he thought of a defense against such an attack by designing the defending vessels with double hulls.

Among Leonardo's other maritime devices were designs for boats that could dredge canals, harbors, and lagoons. What was the result of all these plans? We do not know. Whether any one of them was used against the Turks is a mystery.

At any rate, Leonardo and Pacioli left Venice that same spring and arrived in Florence in April of 1500. One of the purposes of Leonardo's journey was to visit his father who was now living on Via Ghibellina with his fourth wife. Leonardo was now forty-eight. Still tall and straight with the strength of his youth, his face prematurely aged and his hair thinning back from his high forehead, Leonardo was more than ever an outstanding looking man. He still scorned fashionable clothes and dressed according to his own comfort which made him even more noticeable among the crowd. His deep-set eyes with their direct and penetrating glance, framed by his full, reddish beard, never missed a thing, although he now wore spectacles at his work.

Now that he was back in Florence, Leonardo needed lodgings and a job. He had banked his small savings, and he did not want to touch that. His father's house with the five children of his present wife plus the sons from his previous marriages was too full to accommodate Leonardo. Moreover, the relationship between Piero and Leonardo was polite but distant, as Piero preferred the children of his later marriages.

Luckily, the place to live and the commission Leonardo needed presented themselves at the same time. The Church of the Annunciation of the Servite Order of Monks needed an altarpiece, and, as Leonardo's fame was great, they offered him and his apprentice quarters in the monastery. Here, in the solitude of a monastic cell, Leonardo was able to return to his own researches. His long association with Fra Luca Pacioli continued as they worked together on Pacioli's edition of Euclid's *Elements*. At the same time, with his absorption in geometry, Leonardo commenced his studies of the transformation of solids; that is, changing the shape of something to another shape without diminishing or increasing its substance.

In his preoccupation with geometry, Leonardo had apparently done little about the commission which the Servite monks had given him. He finally yielded to their complaints, however, and commenced to draw the preliminary study for the subject, which was "St. Anne with the Virgin and Child." Again his knowledge of geometry is most apparent in the finely constructed composition, every gesture of which is as plotted as a geometric exercise. In April of 1501, the drawing was finished; it caused an immediate sensation throughout Florence. For two days the public was allowed to pass in front of it.

But now a change was taking place in Leonardo. He was no longer content with simply painting. His highly original researches for pictures had slowly grown to the point where the research was more important than painting. In a sense the scientist had taken the brush from the artist. In two letters from Isabella d'Este's emissary in Florence we learn, "He is entirely wrapped up in geometry and has no patience for painting." This excerpt from a letter dated April 8, 1501, was followed six days later by another which said in part, "In brief, his mathematical experiments have made painting so distasteful to him that he cannot even bear to take up a brush."

A few months after the completion of the St. Anne drawing, Leonardo received a letter signed by Cesare Borgia, Duke of Valentinois. Leonardo frowned and thought back to his last days in Milan. When King Louis XII of France had entered the city, he had summoned the painter of the "Last Supper" to an audience. The king had been generous in his praise and had tried to persuade Leonardo to remain. At that same audience had also been Cesare Borgia, an ally of the French. Leonardo remembered the man now—the dark hair and eyes, the black, arched eyebrows, and the face marked by some old disease. He was a powerful-chested, thin-hipped man who had originally been made a cardinal by his father, Pope Alexander VI. But the attractions of secular power soon persuaded him to abandon this title. With the enthusiastic help of his father, Borgia had fought, murdered, and deceived his way to a formidable position of authority in these last years. Leonardo, in the seclusion of the monastery, had lately heard that Borgia's army had even been at the gates of Florence.

The letter addressed to Leonardo was an offer to assume the post of Architect and Military Engineer to IIis Excellency, Cesare Borgia. He thought of Ludovico Sforza—defeated and captured at the battle of Novara just a year ago as he attempted to regain his dukedom. Now the duke was a prisoner at Loches in Touraine; Leonardo had written of him, "The duke lost his State, his personal possessions and his liberty, and none of his enterprises have been completed." And Leonardo also thought of his equestrian monument still standing in the castle being used for target practice by the French archers. Like the duke, nothing of his own had been completed either. Perhaps this Borgia offer was an opportunity. Leonardo decided to accept it.

In May of 1502, after having presented himself to Cesare Borgia in Rome, Leonardo began his hectic travels through Tuscany and Umbria. He was to inspect the fortresses and cities of Cesare's new conquests there, and to make whatever recommendations he felt necessary for their improvements. Arriving in Piombino, he at once set down a project for draining the marshes and reclaiming the land. Also, while he was here, he spent hours by the sea watching the waves curl in from the Adriatic and studying the crash of water over the beaches. Moving on to Arrezzo, he drew up the first in a series of remarkable maps for the army of Vitellozzo which, with the backing of Cesare Borgia, was marching against Florence. These maps are bird's-eye views of Tuscany and Umbria, and somewhat resemble modern aerial photographs. Drawn from Leonardo's own observations, the green mountains stand, according to their height, in relief, with the roads winding over them and down through the valleys. The streams and their tributaries are in blue and even the villages and cities are drawn with great exactitude. Indeed Leonardo had learned his lessons from old Toscanelli well, and he was one of the first to bring the art of cartography to such perfection.

In July and August Leonardo was in Urbino and Pesaro, and by the 8th of August he had reached Rimini. Here he strengthened the fortifications and then rode quickly on to Cesena. Between Cesena, capital of the Romagna, and Porto Cesanatico, he spent from the middle of August to September planning a canal between the two, redesigning government buildings, and drawing up a new quarter to be built for the city of Cesena. At this time he constructed an instrument for telling him the speed of water currents in a stream. It told him whether the flow was swifter at the surface or at the bottom or on one side or the other of the stream's bed.

In the meantime, Florence, alarmed at the growing power of Cesare Borgia, appealed to Charles d'Amboise, Regent of Milan for France, to come to her aid. Charles responded in the absence of the French King and helped to protect Florence. The enemies of Cesare took advantage of this to form an alliance, and soon Cesare was being forced back from his newly won possessions. Cesare himself then hastened to Milan, and there he suddenly came face to face again with Louis, the King of France, who was on his way to Naples. Borgia, who could exert great charm and influence when he wished, persuaded the king that, all rumors to the contrary, he, Cesare, was fighting the enemies of France. Again he won over the French, which greatly strengthened his position. Then, from Pavia, he issued a decree placing every facility possible at Leonardo's disposal. In addition, he instructed all officials to help Leonardo in every matter, referring to him as "our highly esteemed court architect."

While Leonardo was in Porto Cesanatico, a delegation from Bayzid II, Sultan of Turkey, paid a visit to Cesare Borgia. Among other things the delegation was looking for an engineer to build a bridge between Constantinople and Pera to replace a temporary wooden structure. Leonardo designed for them a single-arched bridge with double ramps at either end (looking very much like a present-day "thruway" entrance). He provided that it should be approximately twelve hundred feet long, eighty feet wide, and one hundred and forty feet above the water.

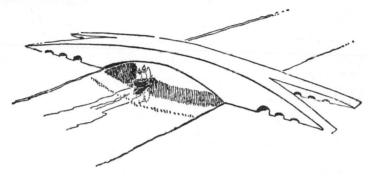

Da Vinci's proposed bridge from Constantinople (Istanbul) to Pera. Looking very much like a modern "thruway" entrance, it was to have double ramps on both sides.

In his travels through the countryside, Leonardo could not help but notice how primitive the mills were. Feeling how strongly the wind blew in from the sea, he designed a windmill with a roof that turned with the sails. For the mechanism inside he devised a band brake —a semicircle of wood into which the large cogwheel of the mill was forced. This mill resembles the "Dutch" mills of the Netherlands and was among the first of its type to be brought into existence.

In the fall Leonardo was at Imola. There he created another of his beautifully rendered maps. He drew this with the help of a magnetic compass of his own invention. It consisted of a board with an arc on it and a compass needle, and was probably the first magnetic needle on a horizontal axis. This time the map was of the city itself, the walls, the castle and the principal buildings all touched with color and the river winding through the fields. Drawn in the shape of a circle, it resembles a view through a telescope from directly above. In Imola, too, he met Niccolò Machiavelli, the famous historian and political scientist, who was an emissary from the Signoria, the Council which now governed Florence. These two men became friends and, later, collaborators in Leonardo's scheme to make the Arno river navigable to the sea.

At this time Cesare Borgia, having achieved great success in his military campaigns and confident of his conquests, decided to return to Rome. With the disbanding of Borgia's headquarters at Imola, Leonardo's duties were finished. Together with his new friend Niccolò Machiavelli and two other Florentines, he left Imola and the service of Cesare Borgia to return to Florence.

In January of 1503, a mathematician named Giovanni Battista Danti attempted a flight in a machine that he had designed. This flight was part of the entertainment at a wedding reception in Perugia. Danti climbed into his apparatus on top of the tower of St. Mary of the Virgin. It was pushed off into the air, hovered a few seconds, then began slowly drifting toward the ground. But suddenly, one of its wings hit a building projection and it crashed. Danti was carried away with a broken leg.

The news of the event traveled quickly to Florence.

When Leonardo heard about it, he eagerly questioned all those who had either seen it or had heard it described first hand. Danti's attempted flight excited Leonardo for now he realized that he was no longer alone in his search. With a sense of urgency he returned to the problems of flying. He felt now that the solution to flight might be in the swift gusts of air through the ravines and the spread wings of the eagle drifting high in the sky.

10

Shattered

Hopes

BEFORE Leonardo could return to the problem of flight, however, he was again faced with the necessity of supporting himself and his growing household. The small fees he received for taking on apprentices hardly covered the cost of housing and feeding them. Moreover, the equipment he had to buy for his scientific researches added further to his strained budget. So, when a servant from Francesco del Giocondo, a rich Florentine merchant, presented himself at the gate with the request that Leonardo accept a commission to paint Francesco's wife, Leonardo was only too glad to accept. The name of Francesco's wife was Madonna Lisa, or Mona Lisa for short. Leonardo painted her portrait on and off for the next three years. Thus, what started as a minor commission ended as the one painting—in addition to the "Last Supper"—that most people today associate with the name of Leonardo da Vinci.

Having secured this work, Leonardo turned back to his studies of birds in flight and the nature of air. The soaring wings of eagles and hawks and the way they rode the currents with hardly a dip of their spread wings guided Leonardo's thinking from pure mechanics to machines that act more on the principle of the glider. He proposed to write a treatise on the nature of birds' flight, and, with his usual thoroughness, he began to weigh, dissect, and reconstruct various types of birds and their wing structure. He realized that one of the main difficulties of gliding was maintaining balance, or, more accurately, maintaining the center of gravity. From previous observations Leonardo had noted that man is capable of making the same motions that a bird does. He had also measured the strength of a man's legs and had calculated that man has twice the power in his leg muscles that he needs for standing. Consequently he began to redesign his machine making use of man's arms and legs to operate or "flap" the wings instead of standing him on a platform.

The first of Leonardo's new designs was a sort of harness apparatus strapped across the shoulders of the flyer who was supposed to be able to keep himself balanced by moving the lower part of his body. He could manipulate the flight by handles that were connected to the flexible, outer parts of the wings. These wings were designed from the webbed wings of the bat. Surprisingly enough, this device closely resembled the experimental gliders used by Otto Lilienthal almost four centuries later in Germany.

Leonardo was now approaching other solutions to pure flight when further hostilities interrupted his work. Florence and Pisa were in bitter rivalry, and their struggle had assumed the proportions of a major war. The Florentine army was now practically at the gates of Pisa. Niccolò Machiavelli urged the Signoria to enlist the help of Leonardo da Vinci, who might be able to think of an immediate plan for destroying Pisa and her army. Never one to think in terms of an immediate battle or a temporary success, Leonardo put forth a daring and sweeping plan that would forever reduce the power of Pisa. The plan was as simple as it was monumental—divert the Arno river from its course into two canals that would empty into the sea at Leghorn south of Pisa. In this way, Pisa would lose her water supply and her opening to the sea.

The plan met with immediate approval and by the end of July 1503, Leonardo was sent out to survey the entire course of the river. He was accompanied by Giovanni "the Piper," a man who was frequently employed on minor engineering projects and who was the official player of the pipes to the city of Florence. Giovanni was also the father of Benvenuto Cellini, who became the most famous goldsmith of the Renaissance. As they made their way to Pisa, Leonardo made some more of his extraordinary maps of the area, paying par-

ticular attention to the course of the Arno and its tributaries. These maps later inspired him to plan a whole
series showing the main watersheds of Italy.

When he rode into the Florentine camp drawn up
before Pisa, Leonardo designed from his observations
and maps, a dam on the Arno to regulate the course of
the river. This bird's-eye view map is a marvel of exact-
ness. It shows the flow of the river hitting the dam with
its swirling backwash and overflow. Leonardo's knowledge of the movement of water was so great and his
craftsmanship in drawing so fine that the water in this
map seems to flow before one's eyes. One of the main
problems in regulating the Arno was its tendency to
continually be shifting its bed by the deposits of new
sediment, and Leonardo realized it would be a long
time before this project could be completed.

When he returned to Florence he presented to the
Signoria, as part of his survey, various machines to
hasten the excavation of the Arno. He had designed a
crane that would assist in the digging out of two different levels at the same time. He also submitted the results of his calculations on the saving of muscular energy
by the use of such machines. In addition, Leonardo
proposed to use the water in the canals for irrigation
purposes and had even calculated what the volume and
velocity of a jet of water would be if projected from an
opening in the bottom of the canal wall into an irrigation ditch. As if this were not enough, he had invented
a practical method of piling as a foundation for the
lock-basins to protect them against the dangers of ero-
sion.

A separate map of this period on the flow of rivers in

general was intended to relate to his treatise on the nature of water. In this treatise is the first outline of the fundamental principles of hydrodynamics, as for example:

The velocity of a current increases with the slope and decreases with the winding of the riverbed.

The volume of a river is in proportion to the width of its bed, the slope and the depth of the water being equal.

The slope and width being equal, the speed of the current is greatest in the deepest part of the river.

The excavation force increases at the narrowest section of the river.

Because of the grumbling of the military commanders at what they considered a waste of time, Machiavelli had to intervene with the Signoria before Leonardo was sent out again with documents of authority to continue with his plans. He spent well into the fall surveying the Arno and in October he was back in Florence.

Meanwhile the fighting between Pisa and Florence had been lessened by two political changes. In August Pope Alexander VI had died and his son Cesare Borgia became seriously ill. The Republic of Florence was now free of its most dangerous enemies—the Borgias. The city relaxed in its new security and the hostilities between Florence and Pisa died down to an uneasy armed watch.

Leonardo quickly took advantage of the situation to present an early dream of his to the Signoria. He again put forth his idea of a commercial canal to the sea and made mention of the great advantages there would be for all the mills, lumber yards, forges and other commercial interests in utilizing the water power that would be available from his project. Piero Soderini, the governor of the city-state of Florence, was impressed and thought of the glory it would bring to Florence and himself. He told Leonardo he would present it to the Signoria.

Leonardo now plunged into a winter of great activity. Forced to draw from his savings, he had rejoined the guild of painters in October of 1503, and then applied for the commission of painting the murals in the council chamber of the Palace of the Signoria. It had been planned to decorate this great hall with scenes commemorating famous Florentine victories, and Leonardo chose the battle of Anghiari where the soldiers of Florence defeated the Milanese in 1440. In addition to working on the "Mona Lisa" and continuing with the canal project—for which he was now designing great suction pumps to lift rivers from one level to another—he turned again to astronomy and geology.

Leonardo, while investigating the course of the upper Arno, had come across much evidence that the land there had at one time been completely under water. Various types of ancient ocean life and vegetation lay scattered in layers along the ridges of the mountains, and these Leonardo collected and brought back to his studio. He wrote, "above the plains of Italy where now birds fly in flocks, fishes were wont to wander in large shoals." He reread Ptolemy, the ancient Greek geographer Strabo, and even Sir John Mandeville, an English author of travel books, in his quest for knowledge of distant places. He talked to travelers, sailors, and wrote to friends to send him information about the countries they had seen or lived in. Strabo, in particular, had set forth the doctrine that the earth's transformation had taken place by the forces of volcanoes and water, but the wisdom of these early men had been obscured by the closed minds of the Middle Ages.

Even in his own time of reawakening knowledge—the Renaissance—Leonardo had to contend with the combined superstition of the Church and the ignorance of misguided scholars. For example, the Church believed in the great flood, as described in the Bible, and the scholars claimed that if what Leonardo said were true—that the earth was the result of an evolutionary process—there would have been written records. To this latter Leonardo responded, ". . . sufficient for us is the testimony of things produced in the salt waters and now found again in the high mountains far from the seas." But Leonardo's conception of the evolution of the earth was mistaken in one respect. He regarded the earth as organic—living—and the flow of water he believed to be like the flow of blood in man. Indeed, according to Leonardo, all living creatures were reflections of a living, breathing earth. It was only when he again turned his eyes inquiringly toward the moon and the laws of the universe that he began to realize his error.

It had been the idea that the earth was the center of the universe which supported Leonardo's theory of an organic earth. Yet after years of observation and study he abandoned this theory and, with the eye of a man centuries ahead of his time, he wrote in his notes, "The moon has every month a winter and a summer. And it has greater colds and greater heats and its equinoxes are colder than ours." He went further and identified the elements existing on the moon such as "water, air, and fire," and described them and their functions as being like those on our own earth. In so doing he recognized the existence of the moon as a solid in space, reflecting the light of the sun—one of many "stars" in a universe. With his acceptance of this concept he realized that the earth could not be organic.

In May of 1504, the Signoria complained to Leonardo that there had been no progress on the proposed paintings for their council chamber, even though he had already been partially paid for them. Accordingly, he was forced to sign a document that he must be finished by February of next year or refund all monies paid him. As was his custom he had made many preliminary drawings. Although he was well acquainted with horses he had again researched their anatomy and actions. Pages of rearing, frightened horses and men in combat covered his studio tables. On one of these pages there are sketches of the heads of a lion, some horses and a man —all with fierce expressions on their faces. Here Leonardo hinted at the comparative anatomy of expression in man and animal that Darwin was to write about almost four hundred years later.

But the paintings could wait, for now the Arno River was in spring flood. The time had arrived to make the first attempts at diverting the river into its new course. Leonardo was again in the field supervising the work. There had been much opposition to Leonardo's canal from both the army captains and the Signoria. It was

called a whim and a crazy idea, but Piero Soderini and
Niccolò Machiavelli were stubborn in their defense of
Leonardo's plan and they overcame all opposition to it.
And indeed, the raising of the sluice gates was successful
and the Arno actually flowed into its new bed. The
tensions in the camp and in the Council of Florence
were eased. The only sad person was Leonardo, for he
had just learned of the death of his father.

Leonardo felt the loss deeply. Outwardly, however,
he only acknowledged the death of his father at a distance. Not only had Leonardo and his father drifted
apart over the years, Piero left nothing to Leonardo in
his will. His father's other children quarreled among
themselves over what money he did leave. Leonardo's
one friend in the family was Uncle Francesco, who was
still living in Vinci. When he heard of his brother's will,
Francesco made out a will of his own and left everything
to the nephew he loved—Leonardo.

After having successfully diverted the Arno river, it
was now necessary for Leonardo to return to the painting commissioned by the Signoria for its council chamber. But recently, Leonardo had suffered a rebuff in this
work. Originally he had been given the whole room to
do but now the opposite wall had been assigned to another man—Michelangelo Buonarroti. Leonardo had
first met the young Michelangelo when he helped to
judge the best location for Michelangelo's monumental
statue of David. The two men were opposites in every
way. Leonardo, fifty-two years old, carefully dressed,
cool and detached, was a man whose every action was
the result of a thoughtful and analytical mind. Michelangelo, twenty-six years old, his clothes rumpled and

covered with marble dust, was passionate and moody—an impulsive youth totally dedicated to art. They did not like each other, and now Leonardo was forced into a rivalry for which he had no heart.

The duel between these two giants of art aroused the whole of Florence and there was a constant stream of people watching them at work. Michelangelo was given a studio in the hospital of Sant' Onofrio and Leonardo was working in the Papal Chamber in Santa Maria Novella. Among the many people who came to watch Leonardo was a young man of nineteen. He was already a pupil of Perugino and the experience of meeting and learning from Leonardo was to influence him the rest of his life. His name was Raffaello Sanzio—one of the great Renaissance painters of Italy and known to us by the name of Raphael.

While Leonardo worked at Santa Maria Novella he had the opportunity of continuing his studies in anatomy. Dissections at that time were novelties and when one was performed the doors were thrown open to the public. Leonardo must have attended the public dissections at the Church of Santa Croce. Now at Santa Maria Novella there was a hospital, and here Leonardo was able to continue his own dissections without interruption. In a cool room below the hospital where bodies were kept Leonardo worked late into the night. By the flickering lights of candles and in the silence of the world about him he studied, drew, and wrote in his notes of the wonders of the human body.

He performed autopsies on people who had died natural deaths—a special permission granted to him by the monks of the church, and among these autopsies are

*In a cool room below the hospital, Leonardo worked late
into the night.*

the first written reports of some of the diseases that are the causes of death. Arteriosclerosis, or stony growths in the blood vessels, and pulmonary tuberculosis, a nut-like growth in the lung, are among the discoveries Leonardo made in his lonely searches, although he did not use these medical names for them.

Above all Leonardo was attracted to the function of the muscles, especially those in the arms and legs. So faithfully, in fact, did he record the origin and insertion of all the various muscles that these drawings can be used as anatomical models today. Moreover, he believed that a good drawing was worth pages of words describing human anatomy. The muscles were rendered as cords so as to better understand their function. He described this function as one of pulling instead of pushing and he noted that for every muscle there is an opposing muscle. When one contracts the other expands. For example, when you tighten the biceps in your arm you can feel the looseness of the triceps, the muscle on the opposite side.

As the end of the summer of 1504 approached, Leonardo's dream of the canal from Florence to the sea was destroyed. The summer had been hot and without rain. The water in the canal dried up and the Arno river returned to its original course. All the old arguments against the plan were revived. The Florentine army captains rebelled against the job of defending a useless project. Again Soderini and Machiavelli intervened. After heated debates in the Council of Eighty, which had been called into special session, Machiavelli himself was sent out to oversee the work. It was brought almost to completion when in late October disaster struck. The rains that had failed to come in summer fell from the heavens in great cloudbursts. Storm after storm swept the valleys. The workmen left and the soldiers were recalled. The Pisan army rushed in to fill up the diggings and one final storm washed away the dream to nothing but eroded mounds of dirt.

Leonardo buried his disappointment in other work. When the drawing for the Battle of Anghiari was ready for transfer to the wall of the council chamber, he had a special scaffolding made of his own invention which worked on the principle of a pair of scissors standing on end, with a long platform on top. As the legs were spread the scaffolding was lowered and when they were pinched together it was raised. The wall had been prepared with a special mixture which he hoped would bring out the brilliance of his tempera colors. With several assistants who had been assigned to him by the Signoria the violence of the Battle of Anghiari was transferred to the wall and the actual painting was begun.

During the winter months Leonardo would relax from his work on the huge painting and his dissections to roam the country around Florence. He visited the slaughterhouses where the animals were killed and prepared for market. Here he was able to examine the hearts of animals just slaughtered and to note that the heart retained its action until the body was almost cold. He made a glass model of the aorta (the main artery leading from the heart) of an ox with which he could experiment on the flow of the blood. He intended to add to it a glass tube for one of the semilunar valves of the heart. He also experimented with a frog, dissecting its brain, heart, and entrails and noted that it ceased to twitch only when the spinal cord was severed. In his notes, he wrote, "The frog instantly dies when the spinal cord is pierced; and previous to this it lived without head, without heart or any bowels or intestines or skin; and here therefore it would seem lies the foundation of movement and life." He was of course searching for the reasons that muscles moved and from where the impulses originated.

One of Leonardo's favorite places to visit was Fiesole where his uncle Allessandro Amadori lived. Uncle Allessandro was the brother of Leonardo's first stepmother and, since he had loved her so much, he likewise felt an affection for Allessandro. At Fiesole, which rises over Florence in a steep ascent, Leonardo could watch the birds circling in the air below him.

On these lofty heights, he would unfold his drawings of flying machines. Leonardo had progressed now to a point where an actual flight was all that was left. He had designed a sort of flying boat—a shell with wings that moved up and down and he had introduced a tail like that of a bird. He had noted that the tail of a bird acts as a rudder, a stabilizer and a brake when landing.

But Leonardo's most recent design was one that was called an *ornithopter*. It consisted of a wooden frame, two huge wings like a bat's, a series of ropes and pulleys and a windlass, all planned with the lightest of materials. The flyer, lying prone in the frame, his feet in leather stirrups connected to the wings by pulleys, would move his feet up and down to flap the wings while, at the same time, he operated the windlass with his arms in order to guide the machine. Soon he hoped to build this machine and try it out.

Meanwhile, Leonardo returned to his painting in the council chamber with impatience, for spring was approaching and the time to finally realize his dream of flying would be at hand. Aside from an assistant who had tested the pedals and windlass, no one knew of his plan to actually put his machine in the air.

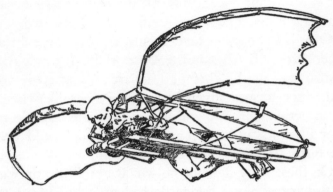

The ornithopter, one of Leonardo's designs for a "flying machine." By pumping his feet in the stirrups, the flyer could flap the device's wings.

Weeks passed and the painting was almost finished. The huge wall was covered with plunging horses and embattled soldiers. The colors were brilliant on the special mixture he had prepared for the wall—but they were not drying as they should have. Something was wrong. To speed the drying process, Leonardo had a special fire built in the room that directed the heat onto the painting. Spectators were allowed to watch as the waves of hot air rose against the wall. Then—disaster began slowly with a small trickle of paint from the top! Before anybody could put out the fire, the great figures and horses slowly melted down the wall in shiny, sticky streaks of color. Leonardo fled the room in an agony of shame.

With his own friends discouraged, the Signoria hostile, and the friends of Michelangelo triumphant, Leonardo went back to Fiesole. He went back with his secret dream of flight. The world would soon forget the Battle of Anghiari—but the conquest of the air, if he could achieve it, would live forever.

In the spring of 1506, from the slopes of Monte Cecero near Fiesole, legend tells us that a great bird sailed into the air and disappeared. No one knows whether Leonardo actually flew his machine or not but Girolamo Cardano, the son of a friend of Leonardo, wrote, long after Leonardo had died, "Leonardo da Vinci also attempted to fly, but he failed. He was a fine painter." Another dream had been shattered.

11

The

Return to Milan

Leonardo felt his fifty-four years that spring day in 1506. The bitterness of his failures and the frustration of his dreams added considerably to the weight of his years. All morning he had wasted in argument with Soderini and the Signoria. If it had not been for the letter from Charles d'Amboise, Viceroy of the King of France for Milan, he would have felt like a beggar. Charles d'Amboise had been appointed military governor of Milan by Louis XII ever since the French had conquered that city and captured Duke Ludovico Sforza. But the authority of the letter had finally won a grudging consent from Soderini. Leonardo looked about him to see if he had forgotten anything and slowly climbed onto his horse. He nodded to Salai, his apprentice, looked back to see if his servant had the pack-horses ready, and started down the street leading the small procession. He was going back to Milan.

Leonardo took out the letter and reread it. The words were respectful and admiring—and in French. They requested the presence of "Maître Leonard de Vinci" at the court of Charles d'Amboise, for purposes of painting and other "diverse projects" for the King of France. The letter restored a measure of confidence to Leonardo's self-respect. Before Leonardo left, Soderini had made him sign a letter in which Leonardo promised to return to Florence within three months and to leave a deposit of one hundred and fifty florins which would be held against his return. It was signed, notarized and dated May 30, 1506. Nevertheless, Leonardo had decided to accept the French envoy's offer; moreover, he looked forward to the prospect of returning to his vineyard at Porta Vercellina and the understanding of a sympathetic patron.

Indeed, Charles d'Amboise turned out to be more than sympathetic. He recognized Leonardo as a great artist; but even more, he was one of the few patrons who could appreciate the magnitude of Leonardo's scientific and mechanical genius. In the court of Charles, Leonardo once more enjoyed a time of peace and an assured income. The French Vice-Chancellor of Milan, Geffroy Carles, who was second in command, was also

a distinguished scholar and a patron of the arts and
natural sciences. With the admiration and support of
these two men and especially with the distant backing of
King Louis XII of France, Leonardo's dismal memories
of Florence began to fade.

Leonardo's three months' allotted absence from Florence, however, were soon past and a letter arrived from
Soderini demanding either Leonardo's return or a for-
feiture of the one hundred and fifty florins deposit. Now
a tug-of-war developed between the Viceroy of Milan
and the governor of Florence over Leonardo. The Signoria reminded Charles that Leonardo had his work to
complete, while Charles d'Amboise and Geffroy Carles
demanded an extension of time. One month more was
granted. More letters were exchanged until the affair became so heated that the King of France himself intervened. In January of 1507 the French King informed
Soderini and the Signoria that Leonardo was "not to
move from Milan until our arrival." Since Florence at
this time was under the protection of the French, such
final authority silenced the Signoria. Shortly afterwards
Leonardo discharged his obligation to the Signoria by
relinquishing the one hundred and fifty florins, and he
at last became free from the demands of his native city.

On May 24, 1507 King Louis XII re-entered Milan
with all the splendor and color that France and the
Dukedom of Milan could confer upon their ruler.
Knights in armor and the ladies of the courts followed
the king who rode in flowing white and gold under a
canopy of blue decorated with the lilies of France.

With such pomp and display in Milan, Leonardo was
soon back at his old occupation of designing pageants

and tournaments. While some of the people from the days of the Sforzas returned, not many remembered Duke Ludovico, who was slowly dying in a French dungeon. Among the people that Leonardo now met, there appeared Francesco de' Melzi, a noble from an old Milanese family, who entered Leonardo's life at this time as a pupil. Soon the young man became like a son to Leonardo. Of handsome appearance, he had the sensitivity to appreciate the essential loneliness of Leonardo and so, almost without realizing it, he filled a gap in Leonardo's life that was to last until the end of his days.

Yet, as Franceso de' Melzi opened one door of Leonardo's life another door closed. He received word that his beloved uncle Francesco had died at Vinci and that he had become the heir to his uncle's property. No sooner had this news been delivered when Leonardo was notified that Giuliano, a son of Piero, and now a lawyer in his own right, was contesting the will. All the frustrations of his life in Florence now rose to an angry pitch and he set out once again for Florence to fight for his own rights.

Wisely, Leonardo had armed himself with letters from his new, influential patrons and even one from King Louis himself recommending, ". . . we request that you will cause this dispute to be settled in the best and briefest delivery of justice . . ." In August of that same year —1507—Charles d'Amboise added his personal letter suggesting that the king could not spare Leonardo too long from the court at Milan.

It was with the title of Painter and Engineer to the King of France that Leonardo rode back to Florence to await the outcome of the judges in his case. He went to stay with a sculptor friend, Giovanni Rustici, a man of thirty-five and also an ex-student of Verrochio. They lived in a house lent to Rustici by a wealthy scholar and patron named Piero Martelli.

Leonardo soon found that he and Rustici had much in common. Rustici, too, collected the odds and ends of his journeys into the country. Flying about the house were a tame eagle and a raven, while, at dinner, a pet porcupine begged for food. Rustici, however, was a believer in alchemy and magic. To practice these arts, the young man devoted one room to the strange mixtures which bubbled over flames as he attempted to change base metals into gold, or to call upon the spirits to predict the future.

Leonardo settled into the life of the house very quickly and even helped his friend on an important sculpture commission. This was a group composition of St. John between the Pharisee and the Levite for over the doors of the baptistry. He also started to gather together his scattered notes on all the subjects that he had written about, going through them making corrections and erasing the repetitions. Possibly Leonardo was considering the publication of all his material for he wrote, "Begun at Florence in the house of Piero di Braccio Martelli, on the 22nd day of March, 1508. This will be a collection without order, made up of many sheets which I have copied here, hoping afterwards to arrange them in order in their proper places according to the subjects of which they treat . . ." This "collection without order" of almost forty years extended into practically all branches of human knowledge, founded on years of observation and experiment. Indeed, it was the magnificent effort of one extraordinary mind to push back the curtains of ignorance in order to let the light of natural truth shine through to mankind.

In addition, Leonardo returned to his studies of anatomy and comparative anatomy. For this latter he made many beautiful drawings of the legs of animals as compared to those of man. With them, Leonardo tried to indicate man's place in the natural order of the world. He pointed out that our physical bodies are basically the same as those of animals, and that the muscular and organic differences are those of function only. For example, bird and man have the same chest muscles, called the pectoralis. But the bird, in order to fly, has developed these into powerful instruments of motion. Man, on the other hand, has learned to stand and move in an upright position. He has developed the muscles of the back, called the erectores spinae, and those of the buttocks to hold him erect. Leonardo intended to enlarge upon his studies of comparative anatomy to include all living creatures, even the insects.

Meanwhile, the Viceroy of Milan was becoming impatient for Leonardo's return. The judgment against his half-brothers had been settled in Leonardo's favor, and he hastened back to Milan. By the summer of 1508 he was once more in the routine of the court's activities. King Louis had granted Leonardo a regular allowance and it was the first time he had enjoyed such a long freedom from the concerns of earning a living. With these steady payments Leonardo now had the leisure and support to pursue his own multitude of interests.

As his notes began to take shape and he thought of printing them, it was natural for the inventive Leo-

nardo to design his own printing press. It is one of the
earliest such designs on record. Because the carrying bed
which held the type and the paper was automatically
adjusted to the handlebar, the press could be operated by
one man. Besides his notes Leonardo also considered
printing a work by Roger Bacon, the thirteenth century
English scientist.

This project for printing his own books, however,
was never realized by Leonardo. Lately, he had received
a commission which took him back in memory to the
days of Ludovico. The subject was Marshal Gian Gia-
como Trivulzio, a soldier-of-fortune. Originally this man
was a loyal commander of Galeazzo Sforza's but when
Ludovico came to power he had had Trivulzio banished
from Milan. Embittered, Trivulzio had become a stubborn enemy of Ludovico from that time on, serving
under any banner that marched against the house of
Sforza. A stocky, square-faced man, his body was covered with the scars of many battles. He had been fighting
with the French ever since the time Ludovico had be-
trayed Charles VIII. Trivulzio had seen the great monument that Leonardo had modeled and, although it was
riddled by French arrows and damaged by wind and
rain, the Marshal was impressed and wished for a similar memorial to himself.

Leonardo set to work immediately. His past experience with the Sforza monument was now to his advantage. This time there was no need for experimenting.
He knew how much material he needed and the approx-
imate cost of everything including the casting. He
submitted an estimate of three thousand and forty-six
ducats for the completed work, one hundred of which

would go to Leonardo. The sum was acceptable to Trivulzio and Leonardo began his preliminary studies.

As he gathered the material for this new equestrian statue, Leonardo and the French Viceroy Charles d'Amboise became interested in the further canalization of the plains of Lombardy. The use of canals and locks had been in practice for roughly a hundred years and around Milan there were already some fifty miles of canals and about twenty-five locks. Leonardo started another survey of the area. In his imagination, he envisioned a vast hydraulic engineering project.

On September 12, 1508 Leonardo announced in his notes the beginning of a book on the nature of water. He had decided to separate this book from the one on hydraulics because it was necessary to separate theory and practice. His pages treating the science of hydraulics, or the practical applications of water power, had reached to "forty books of benefits." By the spring of 1509 he had expanded his notes on the nature of water to include the greatest wave to the smallest raindrop.

Concerning the practical applications of water power, Leonardo put forth many designs for new locks. He introduced new methods of raising the gates by windlasses and chains which could easily be set in motion by one man. But most important is Leonardo's discovery of the use of centrifugal force for draining marshes—the ancestor of the centrifugal pump. When you rapidly rotate a stick in a pail of water, the water spins in a spiral rising on the sides, and, if you rotate the stick fast enough it bares the bottom of the pail. When you remove the stick suddenly, the water continues to whirl as it slowly subsides.

This is basically the same principle Leonardo used to raise the water from a marsh to a level above the sea so that it could be drained away.

The centrifugal pump was also used with a hydraulic screw which converted water power to mechanical power. The force of a stream of water was injected into the base of a vertical cylinder. In the base of this cylinder was a six-bladed propeller mounted on a vertical shaft. The force of the water turned the screw and at the same time the water was forced to rise in the cylinder to an outlet above. The turning propeller revolved the vertical shaft. This shaft, emerging from the top of the cylinder, turned a cogged wheel. This wheel was joined to another cogged wheel mounted on a horizontal shaft, thus providing the mechanical power. Not only is this the forerunner of the turbine, but the use of the propeller, itself, for propulsion in water, was a new idea not to be thought of again until the eighteenth century. For certain types of hydraulic pumps he conceived of the cone-headed mitre valve still in use today.

Leonardo, besides studying the practical applications of water power, explored the very nature of water itself. In his proposed books on this subject he intended to examine why clouds and fog form, why rain falls and the raindrop itself—even how the raindrop is held together. He understood the nature of capillary attraction, which holds the raindrop together, and his notes show us that he was exploring the science of hydrostatics which relates to the pressure and equilibrium of liquids in general.

Now that Leonardo had a steady income and the relief from meeting painting commissions by fixed dates,

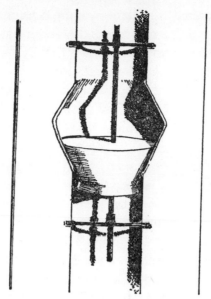

Da Vinci's cone-headed mitre valve for use in a hydraulic pump.

he was free to explore his other favorite avenues of knowledge. It seemed that his ever-active mind could never stop roaming over the whole field of scientific knowledge. He continued with his early interests—the nature and movement of air, astronomy and geometry. He was also still concerned with movement and weight, for he set down in his notes, "The thing which moves will be so much the more difficult to stop as it is of greater weight." This is a hint at a principle formulated by Isaac Newton almost two hundred years later in his First Law of Motion—the law concerning inertia. For example, the motion of an arrow shot into the air maintains itself in flight so long as the influence of the initial force is maintained in it.

On a note dated April 28, 1509 he wrote, "Having for a long time sought to square the angle of two curved sides . . . I have solved the proposition at ten o'clock on the evening of Sunday." As always, Leonardo was deeply involved in the study of mathematics. Too deep perhaps to recognize the new rumblings of war.

Louis XII, still pursuing his campaign in northern Italy, had again arrived in Milan amid the salutes of the French artillery. Following his personal banner of a gold porcupine on a white field, he had come back prepared to do battle with the Venetians whose power, as it diminished in the east, was extending westward into Italy. Alarmed at this Venetian expansion, the French King had allied himself with Pope Julius II and the powers of Europe to form the League of Cambrai to push back this threat. Charles d'Amboise, the French Viceroy, had already taken to the field and at the castle of Cassano, overlooking the Adda river near Milan, he awaited the arrival of his king.

By the end of May, Leonardo was in the saddle once more. Surrounded by the best knights of France and the nobles of Milan, he personally accompanied the French King as military engineer to the meeting with the Viceroy of Milan at Cassano.

During the next three months, through the battles and defeat of the Venetians at Aquadello where sixteen thousand dead were left on the field, and the siege of Caravaggio and the capture of Peschiera, Leonardo served as military consultant and map maker. More than ever his eye was attracted to the possibilities of utilizing the many rivers they crossed both for warfare and commerce. He envisioned making the Adda river navigable from Milan to Lake Como. During this time, he devised not only a revolving bridge but even one of two layers in a single span—the upper level for pedestrians and the lower one for vehicles.

By July, Leonardo had returned with the king and the French army to Milan. Here was planned a great celebration of the French victory over the Venetians. In front of the cathedral, to the delight of the hundreds of spectators, Leonardo devised a mechanical lion scaring a dragon out of an artificial lake into the beak of a cock which picked the dragon's eyes out. After the festivities Leonardo returned to his everyday work. In time, he had a thriving workshop and as he became more and more preoccupied with his scientific explorations, his art commissions were turned over to his assistants. He did continue, however, to work on the plans for Marshal Trivulzio's monument and in his preparatory work for this assignment he expanded his notes and drawings of comparative anatomy.

This renewed interest in anatomy led him to attend a lecture in the winter of 1509. The lecturer was Marc-antonio della Torre, a young man in his late twenties and one of the best-known anatomists of the times. He had been a professor at the University of Padua, but this city had fallen into the hands of the Venetians. Marc-antonio was forced to flee Padua and had settled at Pavia. The two men, when they met, recognized in each other a devotion to science and they began a professional col-laboration that grew into a friendship. Leonardo now developed his anatomy studies to the point where he is today recognized as the foremost medical anatomist of the Renaissance.

Returning to his dissections, Leonardo now proceeded to explore the heart and system of veins in the human body. His drawings of the heart are nearly perfect. Indeed, he was probably the first to discover the endocardium membrane that sheathes the valves and sinews of the heart. Also, he pictured and described the moderator band, "the first cause of the motion of the heart." His work on this organ led him to the doorstep of discovering the circulation of the blood—later to be carried out by William Harvey in the seventeenth century.

Further, Leonardo was the first to accurately draw a representation of the *foetus*, or unborn child, in the womb of its mother, writing in his notes that, "we conclude therefore, that a single soul governs the bodies and nourishes the two." In addition, he drew a remarkable picture of the female figure and for the first time accurately placed her organic structure. In his notes, he also pointed the way to the laws governing metabolism when he wrote, "The body of anything whatsoever that receives nourishment continually dies and is continually renewed . . ." By pouring wax into a hole in the skull he made the first casts of the ventricles of the brain. Several hundred years were to pass before this method was rediscovered.

As Leonardo's work progressed, his admiration for the complexity of the human body grew. Many times in the middle of explaining a section of anatomy he inserted a sentence or two of wonder or praise at the magnificent creation that is the human being. Indeed, these drawings and notes represent the sum of many, many dissections; moreover, Leonardo had to work under conditions that placed many obstacles in his path—the crude lights and instruments, the difficulties of obtaining corpses and, above all, the opposition of the superstitious and ignorant.

The following year Leonardo entered in his notes, "This winter of the year 1510 I look to finish all this anatomy." And yet, however sincerely he might express such a wish, Leonardo was a person who was literally never "finished." The scientific and artistic tasks he had chosen for himself were clearly beyond the limits of any one man. Besides, the pressures of the outside world were once more threatening the peace and quiet of his home and work.

Pope Julius II became increasingly fearful of the French victories over the Venetians. Secretly, he concluded a peace with Venice and, allying himself with his former enemy, he now turned against the French. When the conflict continued, Charles d'Amboise, the patron of Leonardo, was killed at the battle of Correggio. He was replaced by a new French Viceroy, Gaston de Foix. Although the Pope now hired Swiss mercenaries, this invasion from the North was defeated by the young Gaston. Not to be outdone, the Pope then brought in Spanish troops.

In the ensuing bloody battle at Ravenna, the French completely defeated the armies of the Pope and Spain, despite their use of battle-cars armed with razor-sharp sickles on their wheels—strangely like the early inventions that Leonardo designed for Lorenzo de' Medici! Although the French were victorious, they lost their brilliant young leader, Gaston de Foix, and with him they lost their heart. As a result, they were soon disorganized. The Pope's armies renewed their attacks, and the French began a long retreat.

Once again the plague infested Milan and Leonardo's friend, Marcantonio della Torre, died of it. After some futile attempts at recovery, the French fled across the Alps and with them went Marshal Trivulzio. Milan was left temporarily under the martial rule of the Swiss, and Leonardo with only his few apprentices was left again without a patron.

Tired and prematurely old at sixty-one, Leonardo resignedly gathered his possessions together once more and with Francesco de' Melzi and four of his loyal pupils, he turned his back on Milan for the last time. The date was September 29, 1513. Their destination was Rome.

12

Rome

"Name?"

"Leonardo da Vinci."

"Where from and where are you staying?"

"We are coming from Milan by way of Florence. I have quarters being prepared for me at the Belvedere in the Vatican—by order of the Pope. Now, young man, let us pass."

The guard at the Porta del Popolo changed his manner. He dropped his halberd and motioned to the other guards to let the riders through. He touched his helmet roughly and with a grin he said,

"I'm sorry, Sire—but you know how it is. All these

people—there's bound to be them that we don't want
here. Go ahead, your Excellency. Make way there!"

With these words he laid his spear against a jostling
group of broad-hatted pilgrims blocking the entrance
to the city of Rome.

Leonardo heeled his horse and with Francesco de'
Melzi at his side, followed by his servant and students,
pushed past the crowd at the gate. To the left rose the
Pincio hill with its stately pines where, in the days of
Imperial Rome, Lucullus had walked in his gardens.
But Leonardo had no time to look about. It was a damp
December day, and rain threatened from the gray skies.
He was tired, and as Francesco glanced at him he could
see Leonardo pull his cape around him with a little
shiver as the chill wind stirred the long, graying hair
on his shoulders. They made their way through the
crowded, noisy city. They crossed the Tiber and rode
past Castel' Sant' Angelo, the papal fortress built on the
tomb of Emperor Hadrian. After another inspection
by the Swiss guards in beribboned uniforms of white,
green and gold under their shining breastplates, they
entered the walls of the Vatican. That evening after
he had settled himself in the Belvedere apartments and
dinner had been eaten, Leonardo, gazing into the embers
of the fire, looked back over his new stroke of fortune.

The Medicis had returned to power. Pope Julius II
had died, and Giovanni de' Medici, son of Lorenzo, had
become Pope Leo X at the age of thirty-seven. With
his election to the head of the Christian world, the Republic of Florence became a city of the Medicis once
more and Leonardo had received an appointment in
Rome. Giuliano de' Medici, Pope Leo's favorite younger

brother, in his new rise to power and wealth, became Leonardo's patron. The two must have met sometime during the Medici's exile. Leonardo was given the apartments in the Vatican and a salary of thirty-three ducats (approximately eighty-five dollars) a month and a workshop was fitted for him and his pupils. He was also assigned an exclusive German assistant named Georg.

The Pope's court in the Vatican was like the Medici court in the Florence of Leonardo's youth—multiplied by hundreds. Leo X saw himself as the center of the artistic world, and being a man of luxurious tastes with the wealth of the church behind him, the Vatican was soon filled with a mixture of the wise and foolish. Pompous classic-quoters, third-rate poets and clowns mixed with the world's scholars and statesmen. The two greatest artists were Bramante, the architect and friend of Leonardo's first years in Milan, and Bramante's pupil Raphael, the painter.

Bramante was busy building the new church of St. Peter's and, as the architect of this favorite project of the Popes, he was sole master of the Roman art world. Raphael, as his protege, was the recipient of the better painting commissions in Rome. The elderly Bramante and the thirty-year-old assistant were a famous pair in the Rome of 1513. Equally as famous, however, was Michelangelo; he was still living in Rome, but was without patronage after Julius II's death. Leonardo's old rival had scored his triumph with his extraordinary paintings in the Sistine Chapel.

Although the young Raphael, who owed so much to the example of Leonardo, now rode through the streets as a wealthy nobleman, Leonardo himself received no great commissions. While Pope Leo was indulgent of his brother's whims he himself had no use for this tall, serious old man who roamed the shaded walks of the Vatican poking at the strange plants in the botanical garden or making drawings of the foreign animals in the private zoo. In reality, Leonardo's patron, Giuliano de' Medici was a weak man. He played at being a patron but, like his brother the Pope, he lacked the force and decision of his famous father Lorenzo. Nevertheless, he did give Leonardo one small commission for a picture. Immediately Leonardo, excited by the exotic plants in the Vatican gardens, commenced to experiment with them to find a resin to make a varnish with which to cover the future painting. Pope Leo made fun of him exclaiming, to the delight of his court, "This man will never get anything done, he thinks of the end before the beginning."

This ridicule by the Pope made Leonardo a joke to many in the circles of the Vatican who were a little afraid of this strange man with the searching eyes. Leonardo also suffered the humiliations of a man who did not conform to the fashions of his day. His knowledge of Latin, for example, was weak and although he could read it with the help of a dictionary he could not speak it. And, among the people who surrounded the Pope, Latin was the only language allowed. Prizes of great sums of money and important positions were often granted on the strength of an improvised speech in Latin (with many quotations from the classical authors) or a flattering Latin verse. Faced with such setbacks and ridicule, Leonardo—not surprisingly—began to withdraw into himself.

And yet, Leonardo refused to remain idle—he had to work. The need for mirrors in the vast halls and rooms of the papal palace was great. Leonardo turned his mechanical skill to redesigning and improving methods of making them, and even inventing his own machines for the grinding of the glass. Also, for Giuliano, who dabbled in alchemy and magic, he made distorting mirrors and burning lenses. In addition, Leonardo invented a machine which could be run hydraulically for producing long strips of copper of equal width for use in soldering the mirrors.

But, with the making of these mirrors, Leonardo began to run into trouble with his German assistant, Georg. The boy was a loafer; he spoke little Italian and took every opportunity to spend his days with his countrymen in the Swiss guard. Leonardo tried to alter the situation by suggesting that the boy have his meals with him at his worktable, thus giving Georg a better chance to learn the language. This however did not appeal to him. Then, because Leonardo's inventions were so extraordinary, he began to give away the secrets of their mechanisms to Johannes the mirror-maker, another German, who had been replaced by Leonardo in the favors of Giuliano. This naturally made Johannes jealous of Leonardo. Georg gossiped, too, and told stories about the old, eccentric man who lived like a miser in the midst of all the luxury and who drew crazy circles on pages of paper.

These "crazy circles" were geometric exercises that had fascinated Leonardo from the time he had wandered across Italy with Fra Luca Pacioli. Pacioli's book *De Divina Proportione*, containing sixty illustrations from

designs of Leonardo, had been published in Venice in
1509. Leonardo intended to entitle these geometric exercises *De Ludo Geometrico*. In geometry a lune is a
crescent-shaped figure bounded by two intersecting
arcs of circles on a plane or a sphere. Leonardo drew
pages of these lunes and then proceeded to transform
their curvilinear figures into squares of equal area. He
also reviewed Archimedes' method of squaring a circle
and developed it into a variety of ways for cubing
spheres and cylinders.

He returned as well to formulating theories of friction.
He wrote in his notes, "the tallest wheel is the easiest
to pull"—for example, a big wheel turning at the same
speed as a smaller one has less friction to overcome because it makes less revolutions. His experiments in friction predated men like Amontons and Coulomb by two
and three centuries. He established a formula for the
building arch which he described as "a strength caused
by two weaknesses"—if one half of an arch is removed,
the other half collapses. They support and give strength
to each other. In addition, Leonardo determined, before
Galileo, the center of gravity of any pyramid and of a
tetrahedral, or four-sided body.

As the days went by and he waited for commissions
to come, Leonardo took to wandering about the streets
of Rome. He stood in the half-buried Forum of the
Caesars surrounded by grazing sheep and grunting pigs.
Wooden shacks where crude cartwheels were made and
where the marble from the ancient temples was cut and
sold, were built against the sides of crumbling ruins.
The old triumphal arches, now overgrown with creep-
ers, were boarded into towers and cattle were penned

between the shafts of columns that once supported the grandeur of temple roofs. Here and there a classical scholar would be sketching or writing from the worn, Latin inscriptions on a marble slab tilted crazily from the ground where it had fallen hundreds of years ago. Goats wandered on the Palatine hill, once the home of Emperors, and the great baths of the Emperor Diocletian were now a deer park and a hunting ground for royalty.

During the course of these wanderings, Leonardo became interested in the primitive methods of carpentry. Such things as screws, for example, were rare. Those that were used were either made of wood or, if of metal, by goldsmiths laboriously making each one by hand, soldering wire around a pin and another wire into the hole to hold the screw. Sometimes they were made by filing pieces of metal individually. All these methods were time-consuming and costly.

Leonardo had thought of this problem before, and now he concentrated on perfecting his ideas about it. Previously, he had thought of casting the metal in wooden molds and then turning the metal on thread-cutters. The designs he finally drew in careful detail, however, are essentially the methods used today. The new machines did with a few turns of a handle and adjustments of a few cogged wheels what it took one man many hours to perform. He also drew designs for a mechanical plane and a machine for drawing wire that worked by water power.

Leonardo now lived and worked in the Belvedere of the Vatican—more a man on exhibition than an active participant in the great artistic activities taking place around him. True, he received his thirty-three ducats

Leonardo became interested in various methods of carpentry.

a month, but Michelangelo had been paid three thousand for his work in the Sistine Chapel, while Raphael had earned twelve thousand for each room he painted in the Vatican.

Thus Leonardo drifted farther and farther away from his painting. This, in itself, caused people to talk in the papal city. For he had earned fame as a painter, but his passion for science was regarded as strange and whimsical. Occasionally, he did receive a small commission from the workshop of Raphael, yet these were like the crumbs from a rich man's table.

Even the toys Leonardo made at this period for the amusement of his patrons were looked upon as somewhat weird. For example, he would take small pieces of wax and mold them into strange little animals and then inflate them so that they floated in the air in front of a startled guest. Once he caught a curious lizard in the garden and spent hours putting scales all over the tiny body, attached to it a little beard and horns, then let it out from a box at a banquet. The guests jumped back with fear and the women became hysterical.

One of Leonardo's jokes that has been passed down in accounts of his life at this period must have created quite a sensation. He showed the company the cleaned entrails of a sheep resting on the palm of his hand. After telling them to wait and watch he took the entrails in another room and with a bellows inflated them with warm air. As the entrails filled with air they expanded and extended. They crept into the room where the company waited. Slowly they grew and grew until they began to fill the room. The guests overturned their chairs in their hurry to get out of the way of this shapeless, translucent creature. Then Leonardo appeared, the air-filled entrails giving way before him, and said:

"Sires, this is but an example and symbol of virtue. As you can see, the smallest virtue is capable of the greatest growth."

The guests laughed, but it was an uncomfortable laugh. Thus another story was added to the legend of Leonardo as an odd old man.

Leonardo, whose work—particularly his anatomical studies—had constantly been interrupted by the fortunes of war, had found another hospital in Rome where he could continue these studies. This time it was his intention to write a treatise on speech. He dissected and drew the anatomy of the larynx (the voice box), the vocal cords and the trachea (the air passage to the lungs), and all the muscles that control the movements of the tongue and the lips. If you pronounce each letter of the alphabet you will feel these muscles of the lips, especially with the letters "o," "p," and "f." Carefully he noted how the air vibrations from the trachea form themselves into vowels and consonants, and he drew the membrane which, when air is pressed against it, makes the sound "aah."

At this same time he was also busy finishing a treatise on painting which he had begun when he was working on the "Last Supper" for Ludovico Sforza. But it was for his knowledge of military engineering that he was sent to the city of Parma by the Pope on September 25, 1514. Here he stayed at the Bell Inn while examining the fortifications and other defenses of the city.

Leonardo's patron, Giuliano de' Medici, had been appointed governor of this particular area and, since

Pope Leo X was fearful of two powerful countries, France and Spain, he was preparing the papal territory against possible invasion. Another fear of the Pope— and indeed of everybody in Rome—was malaria, the disease carried by the mosquitoes that bred in the Pontine marshes west and southwest of the city. At that time, however, no one knew the cause was mosquitoes; rather, they thought it was the bad air from the marshes.

As Leonardo had already been effective in draining the pestilential marshes of Piombino for Cesare Borgia and, later, those around Milan for Charles d'Amboise, he was assigned the same task for the Pontine marshes. He surveyed the entire area to the sea and made another extraordinary aerial type map. His recommendations included draining the entire area, enlarging and regulating the Martino river and cutting an extra outlet from the river Livoli to the sea. These plans were adopted some years later and parts of the marshes were drained successfully, yielding new land for the cultivation of crops.

By December of 1514 Leonardo had finished his treatise on speech and, possibly in an effort to attract the attention of the Pope, he submitted it to the Privy-Chamberlain, Battista dell'Aquila. As Pope Leo was surrounded by an army of secretaries and assistants who passed on everything submitted, this manuscript with its beautiful drawings was mislaid and lost and only a few notes and sketches remain.

The continual discouragement of his life in Rome was offset by a visit from his half-brother, Giuliano, around Christmas. Leonardo was held in esteem by his family despite the quarrel over his father's and his uncle Francesco's will, and his half-brothers were pleased to tell of their famous relative who lived in the Belvedere as guest of the Medicis. Yet they knew little of Leonardo's scientific dreams and his lack of recognition in the papal city.

Often, Leonardo's greatest comfort was to return to his notes. The challenge of geometry and the mysteries of the movement of air and water kept him from brooding about his lonely life. Francesco de' Melzi, Leonardo's young friend, had more and more taken over the practical responsibilities of his everyday life. Except for his workshop, where the troublesome Georg worked at the making of mirrors, and an occasional small commission for a painting, Leonardo was free to study.

In addition to his geometrical investigations, Leonardo now experimented with the science of *statics* (objects that are stationary), and *dynamics* (objects in motion). One of his most important discoveries in the science of mechanics came about during this period. Concerning the division of weight, he wrote, "There are three conditions of gravity of which the one is its simple natural gravity, the second is its accidental gravity, the third the friction produced by it. But the natural weight is in itself unchangeable, the accidental which is joined to it is of infinite force, and the friction varies according to the places wherein it occurs, namely rough or smooth places." Thus he realized and formulated what composes the movement of an object. He found that movement is the result of separate forces acting upon the object from different directions, as for example, the initial push, the pull of gravity and the resistance of friction. And, before Galileo, Leonardo further experimented with objects dropped from a height. As the result of repeated experiments, he noted that the fall was being affected by the earth's rotation. That is, the object dropped always fell in a slight eastward direction rather than vertically downward—a fact later proved conclusively by Isaac Newton and Robert Hooke in the next century.

He also became fascinated with spiral motion, such as is found in a spinning top or in a whirlpool of water. Because of his interest in *hydrodynamics*, or the movement of water, he began to sketch imaginary "Deluge compositions." These were drawings showing the world—probably inspired by the Bible—in a chaos of wind and floods. They were based on his years of scientific research. Indeed, his drawings of actual whirlpools are still among the greatest of his scientific art. Today, with all the latest technical aids, such as dusting a whirlpool with powdered rosin and then photographing it, an accurate three-dimensional picture is impossible. Yet Leonardo, by sheer observation and analysis coupled with his genius for drawing, could reproduce the complicated shape of whirling water.

In the relatedness of his explorations of water, air and movement, and weight, he worked out the similarity between the laws of equilibrium controlling solids and liquids. The equation between the motive force and resistance that makes for equilibrium or balance in solids can be compared to the equation between the upward pressure of liquids and the downward pressure exerted on them.

Far into the night Leonardo worked on his papers. He tired more easily now, and his eyes had grown weaker. To provide the increase in light that his failing eyesight demanded, he had improved on his original oil lamp by making the wick rise as the oil was burned away, and he had extra lamps fitted to the ceiling.

On January 9, 1515 Leonardo wrote in his notes, "Il Magnifico Giuliano de' Medici set out on the ninth day of January 1515 at daybreak from Rome, to go and marry a wife in Savoy. And on that day came the news of the death of the King of France (Louis XII)." This meant that his new patron had left and his old patron had died. Leonardo's note was a sad one and perhaps he felt, in the departure of his patron, more alone than ever in the crowded life of the Vatican. Giuliano, on the urging of his brother, was marrying Philiberta of Savoy, in an effort to strengthen the prestige of the Medici. Louis XII, before he died, had formed a league against Spain, and with the marriage of the Pope's brother to a noble house of France, the league would be strengthened by keeping the Pope on the side of France. Actually Pope Leo was playing both sides, for at the time he was also friendly with Spain.

Shortly after Giuliano's departure from Rome, Leonardo fell ill, presumably from a mild heart attack complicated by a touch of malarial fever. The doctor had been called. It was a warning, the doctor told Francesco de' Melzi, and Leonardo must remain quiet for quite awhile.

By the end of the winter Leonardo was back on his feet and apparently feeling completely well again.

Giuliano himself had fallen ill about the same time and the news that he had recovered and was finally returning to Rome cheered Leonardo. He sat down and wrote a long letter to his patron expressing his joy. This letter also included a long list of complaints against Georg and Johannes. Georg was now using his room in Leonardo's apartment to do work for others. He lied to Leonardo and flew into such a rage when he was questioned that no one could go near him. Moreover, Johannes, the mirror-maker, was now moving back into the Vatican and turning out mirrors for everyone, even using Georg's room as his own workroom. Johannes boasted of his skill and told everybody that Leonardo did not know what he was doing. Thus, it was not surprising that Leonardo, in his long complaint, was taking out the anger and frustration he felt against all the injustices of his life in Rome.

But by summer Leonardo was again employed as a military engineer. Francis I had succeeded to the throne of France. The new French King was anxious to secure his lost title to the Dukedom of Milan and was preparing another invasion of Italy. Pope Leo X, still trying to play both sides at once, was making secret agreements with Francis while at the same time joining the King of Spain, Milan, Genoa, and the Swiss in an alliance against France. Consequently, he sent Leonardo out to inspect the fortifications of Civitavecchia, a city on the Tyrrhenian coast not too far from Rome. When, in August, Francis I crossed into Italy with an army of thirty-five thousand men including Marshal Trivulzio, the Pope ordered his brother, Giuliano, to take command of the papal forces. On the way to assume this command,

Giuliano fell ill and collapsed. His sickness this time was soon to be fatal.

Leonardo returned to Rome with his survey of Civitavecchia, where he immediately learned of his patron's latest illness. Perhaps realizing that Giuliano was fatally ill, Leonardo made a desperate effort to gain the recognition he felt should be his. He entered the competition for a new façade of San Lorenzo in Florence. Among the other competitors was Michelangelo, his younger and yet oldest rival.

In October of 1515, Francis I had recaptured Milan and by Christmas was in Rome. Leonardo may have met the new King of France in Bologna where Pope Leo X had personally traveled in order to settle a peace treaty with France. Certainly it is known that he attended Francis' court in Rome. Leonardo's name was well respected in French circles and, as Francis had already admired the pictures by Leonardo, the meeting was a happy occasion for them both. Indeed, the recognition that Leonardo had sought in his native land was never as great as that accorded to him by the French.

As Francis I prepared to leave for France in January he must have offered Leonardo a position at his court. While he still hoped that Giuliano de' Medici would recover from his illness and return to Rome, Francis' offer gave him support in the knowledge that he had a powerful, new friend.

March of 1516 brought the first of three events that were to change the course of Leonardo's last years. Giuliano de' Medici died, leaving Leonardo not only without a patron, but without a friend in the Vatican. Now sixty-four years old, he was reluctant to leave his comfortable quarters in the Belvedere with its workshop and pleasant gardens. Besides, deep within himself, he felt that Rome could still offer him the fame that had always escaped him.

Spring ripened into summer and the second event occurred. The competition for the new façade of San Lorenzo in Florence was won by Michelangelo. To Leonardo the news was a blow. The success of his old rival weakened his position in the Vatican even further and added to the growing hostility he had felt in the people surrounding the Pope.

The third event was the sum of many small events. Georg and his friend Johannes, in their jealousy, had spread much gossip about Leonardo in court circles. They now took advantage of Giuliano's death to circulate stories about Leonardo's dissections of bodies in the hospital. These were added to vicious gossip that Leonardo was pro-French. This news eventually reached Pope Leo X. The Pope himself was perfectly aware of the practice of dissection and, personally, he had turned his eyes the other way. However, as dissection was contrary to Church doctrine, an official complaint to the head of the Church could not be ignored. The Pope used it as an excuse to be rid of this tiresome old man whom he had tolerated only for his brother's sake. Leonardo was abandoned.

The year 1516 was drawing to a close. Leonardo had decided to seek the patronage offered him by Francis I. So he and Francesco de' Melzi, his loyal young friend, left Rome for the long journey into France. As he left his native land for the last time, Leonardo looked back over his years—from the silver lute that had sent him to Milan, to the death of Giuliano, to the final rejection of Pope Leo X. Remembering how Lorenzo de' Medici had sent him to Ludovico so many years before, Leonardo thought to himself with great sadness, "The Medici created and destroyed me."

13

The

Last Years

LEONARDO looked around from where he was leaning on the parapet of the Chateau d'Amboise to watch a group of young lords and ladies playing croquet on the emerald-green lawn. The click of the mallets and balls was mingled with the shouts and laughter of the young people. It was late afternoon in May and although the sun was warm the breeze from the west was chilly. Leonardo looked down again from the sheer height of the castle wall across the wide sweep of the Loire river and the valley extending as far as the eye could see. Swallows were swooping low over the banks below and the wind carried their shrilling cries up to him. The forested islands and sandbars interrupted the steady flow of the river and Leonardo could see the reflections sway in the current. He had been studying the river but he realized that his aging eyes were not up to the task of concentrating for long. The wind made them water, so he turned away and started back to his home.

There was much that was familiar in the castle at Amboise. The thick, high walls and round towers and especially the graceful, lacy spires of the king's residence brought back much that he had known in his native land. The gardens had been planted by Italians—there were orange trees and even a mulberry tree from his beloved plains of Lombardy. The king's residence and chapel had been constructed and the decorations carved in stone by Italian artisans. Leonardo could stop and talk in his native tongue with many of the men employed by the king. Since the time of Charles VIII, the French had brought in the latest Renaissance styles from Italy. Leonardo's steps took him back from the castle grounds and down a path with a hand-railing. The steep roofs of the town of Amboise with their chimneys could be seen below him. The path led to a small manor house, like a miniature castle with sharp spires and lacy, carved-stone gables that was set in green lawns and gravel paths.

The Manoir de Cloux, as Leonardo's house was called, had been a hunting lodge for Francis I, but when Leonardo had arrived he gave the house to Leonardo for his home. Francis, in his admiration for this great

Leonardo at Chateau d'Amboise on the Loire.

man, also gave him seven hundred crowns a year, together with a pension of four hundred for Francesco de' Melzi.

The long journey from Rome had left Leonardo tired and weak and he had fallen ill again shortly after his arrival. This time the attack was more serious and had left him with his right hand permanently crippled. He looked at it now as he opened the door to his room. "Another warning," he thought, "and there's still so much to do."

The young, robust King Francis was everywhere at once. He gloried in knightly tournaments, hunts, and sports of all kinds. Always restless, he might appear at any place unannounced. Frequently there would be a clamor at the gates of Leonardo's home and the king would ride in with one or two of his nobles. With a great jingling of spurs he would bound up the stairs of the manor house calling for Leonardo. He delighted in long talks with the old man, and would listen respectfully as Leonardo, his deep-set eyes brooding over his notes, would demonstrate some scientific point on a blank sheet of paper.

At this time, Leonardo was engaged on three projects which demanded his immediate attention. One was the entertainment for a banquet that Francis was giving for his sister, Marguerite de Valois, and her husband. Another was a new design for the king's castle at Amboise, and the third was a design for making a navigable waterway from Amboise to Romorantin. Although these three projects were the main ones that occupied Leonardo's time, there was always the supervising of his pupils' painting on the walls in the little chapel of the manor house, his own work on a painting of St. John the Baptist, and the continual ordering and revising of his notes.

The banquet took place in October of 1517, and the mechanical lion Leonardo had made was an immediate success. It "walked" by means of a spring motor, into the hall, opening and closing its fierce mouth while swaying its head from side to side. With a wand that he had been given, Francis I stepped down from his seat and tapped the lion three times. The toy fell apart and from it a cascade of white lilies poured out at the king's feet.

Also at this time there was a distinguished guest at the castle of Amboise. He was a fellow-countryman of Leonardo and his name was Cardinal Luigi d'Aragona. With him was his secretary Antonio de' Beatis. As Leonardo was now a famous member of King Francis' court, the cardinal paid him a visit accompanied by Antonio. The extraordinary anatomy drawings and all his notes were shown to the cardinal; he and his secretary were deeply impressed. They were also surprised to learn that Leonardo had never been accorded the same recognition by his own countrymen. Antonio de' Beatis wrote home that "This gentleman has written a treatise on anatomy, showing by illustrations the members, muscles, nerves, veins, joints, intestines and whatever else is to discuss in the bodies of men and women, in a way that has never yet been done by anyone else. All this we have seen with our own eyes; and he said that he had dissected more than thirty bodies, both of men and women of all ages. He has also written of the nature of water, and of divers machines, and of other matters which he has set down in an endless number of volumes, all in the vulgar tongue [meaning Italian not Latin], which, if they be published, will be profitable and delightful."

By now Leonardo had accumulated thousands of pages of notes, and they lay stacked in all manner of chests and boxes. Often now, as Leonardo surveyed the work of his lifetime, he realized that he would never see the day of their publication. Time was slipping through his fingers. Already summer had come and gone and now the sharp winds of fall were lifting the leaves from the ground in dancing whirls. Fortunately these were years of peace and for the first time in a long while the people were free of wars. The scheme to canalize the waterway to Romorantin had grown to a vast idea for making a thoroughfare of water from the Loire river all the way down France to Lyons and then into Italy! Leonardo, old and ailing as he was, had surveyed parts of the rivers Loire and Cher, braving the rough roads and crude accommodations.

In addition, Leonardo had designed a castle for Francis I's widowed mother in Romorantin. This castle was never built, but many of the ideas that Leonardo had incorporated in its design were used in the gigantic and magnificent castle of Chambord. Also, at Francis' request, he had reviewed the work being done at the castle in Blois and there is reason to think that the beautiful outside stairwell that spirals from left to right might have been designed by Leonardo.

In February of 1517, a son had been born to Queen Claude and Francis I. The king decided to postpone the baptism of the dauphin (the title given to the eldest son of a French King) until May of the following year. At that time there would be a double celebration at Amboise, for a nephew of Pope Leo X, the young Lorenzo de' Medici, was being married to Madelaine d' Auvergne. As usual, Leonardo was given the assignment of preparing the festivities. Although he was fond of preparing these entertainments, Leonardo now felt the pressure of time; for indeed, the interruptions of this eager young king were sometimes a hardship. He felt that his years were drawing to an end. His notes were unfinished and his dreams of extending man's knowledge of his world and of himself were hindered not only by such petty chores but also by the limits of his own physical endurance.

As Leonardo was sketching one day from the window of his room where he could see the castle walls and the chapel of Saint-Hubert, he set aside the drawing for a moment to write a memorandum to himself. "Write of the quality of time as distinct from its mathematical divisions." Was this extraordinary man sensing the road down which Einstein—in his studies of relativity—was to travel hundreds of years later?

Spring arrived again and with it came the first wild flowers and roses, the songs of the birds in the woods and the blossoming of the chestnut trees. The time for the double celebration came, too, and Leonardo was seen busily preparing the decorations and mechanical delights for the large crowds already assembling. In addition to the tournaments-at-arms that so delighted the king, there was to be a mock battle with a besieged city, and for this Leonardo had had constructed imposing castle walls of wood with a backdrop of a city's spires and towers. The party lasted for weeks, and the climax was performed on the lawns of Leonardo's house where a great ballroom had been set up. Here he repeated an earlier success, the one that had so enchanted Ludovico's guests so many years ago in the Sforza castle at Milan. There was again a dome over the ballroom across which the stars moved mechanically and artificial figures representing various gods and goddesses spoke and sang by means of a hidden choir, while the sun and moon shone in their own lights.

This display ended the festivities. It was already late June and Leonardo was anxious to return to his plans for the water route to Italy. There was the area near Sologne which, when flooded, would make the surrounding countryside a marshland. This would have to be drained by the same method as he had planned for the Piombino and the Pontine marshes. Francis I was interested, too, in the improvements Leonardo had suggested for his own castle, and he would have to talk with the castle superintendent about them. As always, there seemed to be so many things to do, to plan, to work on. Then Leonardo wrote in his notes: "On the 24th of June, the day of St. John, 1518, at Amboise, in the palace of Cloux . . ." and underneath, "I will continue—"

"*I will continue—*" It was almost a note of defiance against the obstacles of advancing age and sickness and the interruptions of the practical world.

The sound of jingling spurs and bridle chains and the snorting of many horses announced another surprise visit from the young king. Leonardo could hear him below shouting something to Battista, the servant who had come to Amboise with Leonardo. Now, as usual, Francis was running up the stairs with all the energy of youth shouting for "le maître" (the master). Resignedly and with patient humor, Leonardo stepped out to greet the king. The gold chains around Francis' thick neck and over his broad chest glinted in the semi-light of the hall, and he was holding his plumed hat at his side and mopping his forehead with a dainty embroidered handkerchief.

"Master Leonardo! We are going on a tour of the river and I want you to look at the place that I told you about. Where I want to put that bridge. You remember?"

"Sire, give me but a moment to gather some material together."

A chest was made ready and soon Leonardo was at the door, calling to Francesco and Battista to help him into the saddle of his horse, while the king's servants hoisted the chest onto one of the carts already piled high with tents and provisions.

When Francis was restless—which was often—a "tour" could mean many hours or many days of travel. Wagons were always kept ready with all the equipment for a long journey and Leonardo, himself, had learned to accept these sudden whims and kept chests of his own ready for any such trip. Now, as always, the king kept his horse reined back out of regard for this tall, stooped man with the long beard and simple clothes.

Yet when Leonardo returned from this "tour" he realized that he could no longer make such trips. The hardships of sleeping in tents, riding over the hot roads, and the necessary work involved in surveying the possible sites for a bridge had left him almost exhausted. He had made one suggestion, however, and that was to build houses that could be carried and then assembled with a few wooden locking devices, then just as quickly taken down and moved to the next place. They could also be left standing where the country people could use them while the court was away. Indeed, such structures would seem to be the ancestors of our own prefabricated houses.

The winter of 1519 was a bitter one. When the cold fog spread over the valley shrouding the bare trees it chilled the big, white-washed rooms of Cloux. The wind blew down from the north sending blasts down the chimneys and scattering ashes and sparks. Leonardo, huddled against the huge fireplace with its roof projecting into the room, pulled his black cloak lined in soft leather around him and reminded himself to include it in his will for Mathurine, the faithful domestic who cooked for him and took care of his house.

The aged Leonardo, who had observed and analyzed so much of man and nature, knew now that his own days were numbered. When the first, pale sunlight of March shone through the small leaded-glass windows of his house, he applied to the king for permission to make out his own will. French law demanded that the property of any foreigner dying in France went to the Crown. The permission was granted, and on April 23, 1519, Guillaume Boureau, the Royal Notary of Amboise was summoned with witnesses.

To his half-brothers in Florence Leonardo left his property at Fiesole and four hundred ducats. To his faithful friend and companion, Francesco de' Melzi, nobleman of Milan, Leonardo willed his notes, drawings, and paintings. Battista was given the income that Louis XII had granted Leonardo from the tolls of the canal at San Cristoforo near Milan. Mathurine was granted the "good black cloth, trimmed with leather" and two ducats. Moreover, Leonardo outlined in detail the plans for his own funeral, right down to the use of ten pounds of candles.

Too weak now to stand any more, Leonardo was confined to his big four-poster bed with the canopy. From it he could see the tracery of the Chapel of Saint-Hubert against the pale, foreign sky through the little window in the corner. The vicar of the church of Saint-Denis was called, with two priests and two Franciscan friars, and Leonardo received the last sacraments at his bedside.

An entry in his notes reads, "While I thought I was learning to live, I have been learning how to die." But death was not easy for him. With tears rolling down his sunken cheeks for "his wasted life," he died on May 2, 1519—fighting even this final interruption to all his work.

King Francis I, who was at St. Germain-en-Laye with his court, wept when the news was brought to him. Francesco de' Melzi was so overcome with grief that he waited until June before writing to the half-brothers of Leonardo of the Master's death. He wrote, in part, "He was to me the best of fathers, and it is impossible for me to express the grief that his death has caused me. Until the day when my body is laid under the ground, I shall experience perpetual sorrow, and not without reason, for he daily showed me the most devoted and warmest affection."

And in a closing paragraph Francesco added these words: "His loss is a grief to everyone, for it is not in the power of nature to reproduce another such man."

14

Mankind's Debt
to Leonardo

WHEN Leonardo died his notebooks began their separate journeys into obscurity. They traveled to different lands and became parts of widely disparate collections. It has only been within the last fifty years that efforts were made to bring them all together between the covers of one volume—a dream that Leonardo himself entertained but never realized. As the manuscripts and drawings were brought to light, translated and published, the extraordinary scope of Leonardo's scientific explorations was revealed.

Mathematician, anatomist, botanist, astronomer and geologist form only part of the long list of his accomplishments and give the clue to the man who considered all the natural world within his province of study. Because of the universality of Leonardo's scientific thought he has been frequently mentioned as the forerunner of such men as Galileo Galilei, Sir Isaac Newton, James Watt, Francis Bacon and William Harvey. Although Leonardo cannot be credited with the actual discoveries that these men made, his methods of investigation pointed the way down the paths that they would follow.

The key to Leonardo's methods lies in a quotation from his notes on vision. He wrote of vision as *saper vedere*—"to know how to see"—and he referred to the eye as "the window of the soul." Again and again, he stressed the importance of observation and personal experience. Although he himself was well read, he emphasized that "science comes by observation not by authority." His supreme talent for drawing underlines his credo and is inseparable from his science. What he saw in the natural world about him needed investigating. The results of these investigations were transformed into drawings as the most certain method for passing this knowledge along to others. The best example of this attitude is represented by his anatomical studies. To merely draw the living figure in front of him was not sufficient—it was imperative to know what he was drawing. He turned to the dissecting room and after intensive study produced some of the finest anatomical drawings in the world—and among the easiest for others to understand.

What Walter Pater wrote of the Renaissance—"in many things great rather by what it designed or aspired to than by what it actually achieved"—could be a summation of Leonardo's own lifetime of effort in science. He labored to bring mankind from the morass of medieval superstitions onto the firm ground of natural facts. With an insatiable curiosity Leonardo attempted the impossible task of encompassing all knowledge. Thus he established his right to immortality—for it was an attempt that shone like a beacon in a world dark with ignorance.

Significant Dates in Leonardo's Life

1452   April 15. Birth of Leonardo.

1467   Commences apprenticeship with Verrochio in Florence.

1478   Commissioned for altarpiece in the Palace of the Signoria.

1481   Commissioned to paint an altarpiece for Convent of San Donato.

1482–83 (?)   Leonardo leaves Florence for the court of Ludovico Sforza in Milan.

1483   Begins equestrian monument of Francesco Sforza for Ludovico.

1484–86   Plague in Milan.

1490   April 23. Recommences equestrian monument and starts book on light and shade.

1496   Meets with Fra Luca Pacioli, professor of mathematics.

1498   *The Last Supper* completed.

1499   Apr. Land awarded to Leonardo near Porta Vercellina. Oct. French occupy Milan. Dec. Leonardo leaves Milan with Pacioli.

1500   Leonardo arrives in Mantua. Travels to Venice and returns to Florence.

1502   In the service of Cesare Borgia.

1503   Returns to Florence, commences work on a canal to sea.

1504   Begins the painting of battle of Anghiari. Father dies. Attempt at flight (?).

1506   May. Leaves Florence for Milan at summons of Charles d'Amboise, French military governor.

1507   Sept. Goes to Florence to settle father's will.

1508   July. Returns to Milan.

1511   Works with Marc Antonio della Torre on anatomical research.

1512   French lose Milan.

1513   Leonardo leaves Milan for Rome. Serves Giuliano de' Medici, brother of Pope Leo X.

1516   Leonardo leaves Rome for France to serve King Francis I.

1519   May 2. Death of Leonardo.

Index

164

IMMORTALS OF SCIENCE

Photos Courtesy of Burndy Library, Norwalk